THE

THE GATES

BY
LESLIE MILDINER
AND
BILL HOUSE

Centerprise acknowledges the help of the Greater London Arts
Association

Published and distributed on behalf of the Stepney Basement
Writers' Group by Centerprise Publishing Project, 136 Kingsland
High Street, London E8

ISBN 0 903738 13 9

Typeset by Jenny Pennings
Printed by Expression Printers Ltd, 5 Kingsbury Road, London
N1 4AZ

CONTENTS

PREFACE

The co-authors of 'The Gates' are both members of a group of young writers, 'The Basement Writers', who meet every week in the basement of the old Town Hall in Cable Street, Stepney, London, E1, to discuss and develop their work. When we first read and discussed 'The Gates' at the Basement, we were impressed by its originality and importance, and at once decided, as a group, that it should be published and read widely as quickly as possible. We specifically wanted it published and distributed locally, so that its readership could be in particular, the local youth that the two authors form a part of themselves. Our own funds were very small and produced by ourselves, and we soon found that money was unforthcoming from public agencies set up in London to provide for the growth of 'culture'. Indeed, the streets of East London, with all the massive talent there unrecognised, unpublished and unread, are still generally unwatered by public 'Arts' money, while the theatres, concert halls, opera houses, fashionable prestige projects and avant-garde studios to the west continue to thrive with healthy subsidies.

However, there was still Centerprise in Hackney, and there the manuscript received the respect, criticism and practical assistance necessary for its publication. Centerprise is a bookshop, coffee bar and community centre which also encourages and publishes local writing. In the past year it has published many books of poetry and stories, some by children, others by local adults, as well as a series of local working class autobiographies. With the addition of 'The Gates' quite a substantial body of work has been published, which in many ways challenges conventional assumptions about what kinds of people have a right to produce a 'literary culture'. Without exception, all of these books have been written by people without any form of further education, yet they form a very powerful and moving body of writing. The public bodies who are supposed to encourage the growth of 'culture' have so far remained deaf to the many voices which arise out of the less glamorous parts of our cities and towns. They cannot any longer choose to ignore the growing demand for a more equitable distribution of financial resources that are being made available for 'the arts'.

The Basement Writers
October 1974

INTRODUCTION

Why did we write a book about School Phobia and Agoraphobia? Well, there are thousands of people who have these phobias yet very little is written about them. Because they are phobias, people automatically think that it has nothing to do with the so-called 'man in the street', it is a word used only by psychologists, or writers of certain problem pages in women's magazines. Well they are wrong. Everyone has a phobia of some sort. From a morbid fear of mice, to the more socially noticed ones such as Agoraphobia. So we decided to go into them in more detail, and describe how it really is. I hope we have achieved this.

Years ago children who 'played truant' were classed as 'badly behaved' or 'lazy'. And if they were truants for very long they came to the same inevitable end. They were taken *into care*. School Phobia comes under neither of these categories. It is a mental illness, an illness that if left to grow can lead to a shattering nervous breakdown. But please, don't get me wrong. Only a small minority of truants have this phobia. There is all the difference in the world between the twelve year old boy being sick first thing in the morning at the thought of school and the fifteen year old who is just fed up with the whole system, for that is a different problem entirely, although just as widespread. Nevertheless, this minority needs help and it needs help *now*.

When I was ill I remember thinking I was the only person in the world with a problem like mine. So we wrote this book to show phobics that they are not alone, and there is hope. And above all, to show parents that when their child will not go to school no matter the consequences, then he or she may not just be having 'that Monday morning feeling' or 'lazyitis'.

Although this book sometimes has a humorous slant the core of it is very serious indeed. It is based upon true-life incidents, upon things that have happened to us and to people we know, and for obvious reasons the names are changed. Now on to a lighter vein. It seems that one of the things about 'The Gates' that intrigues people the most is the fact that two people wrote it without arguing so much that they couldn't carry on. Well we did argue, and there were times when we just wanted to forget about the whole thing. But we persevered and succeeded, and I hope the next book isn't as hard to write. A lot of people have asked us how did we go about starting the book. Well I must confess, I didn't start it, Bill did.

For about six months before the start of the book he had been saying that we should write one about our experiences at our many schools. But I didn't take him seriously (much like the people who didn't believe that we would write this book) then one day he turned up with the first part of 'The Gates' and I'll be truthful, I thought it was terrible, and that was how we started. Being bigheaded I thought I could do much better, and I wrote my idea of the first chapter, and for the next six months that's how it went. Bill would write his idea of a chapter (after making a plan of the whole book) then I would rewrite it putting my ideas in. Sometimes a chapter would have to be written four or five times until we had it right. Then we would give our scribble to our dear friend Liz Jackman, and a few weeks later she would give us back a superbly typed-out counterpart that her mother Betty had kindly offered to type for us, as then neither of us had used a typewriter.

Anyway, enough of my chatter. Here it is. I hope you like it.

L. M.

CHAPTER I

WHEN THE SHELL OPENS

Geoffrey Moller approached the gates of Elgan Comprehensive School. He hated those gates. He hated everything to do with school. How he dreaded those mornings when he sat nervously on the corner of his bed and literally shook with fear, for he knew that if he kept on playing truant, he would be taken 'into care'.

Geoff had an uncontrollable fear of school, a fear that grew with every thought of attending it. He could only put it down to the change from Primary School to Secondary Education. At one time he had been safe, safe inside the shell of Stanford Primary School. But now—that shell had opened, and Geoff was released from its womb and let out into the noisy, rough hell-world of Elgan Comprehensive—a world he was not ready for.

Geoff had been attending Elgan, on and off, for about a year. During that time he had been experiencing attacks of dizziness. The first time Geoff could remember undergoing the dizziness, was when he was standing in the playground, watching some boys playing football. All of a sudden everything was like a dream. He had never felt so strange in all his life. Geoff knew he was in the playground, but it just didn't seem like it. It was as if he was watching someone else on a film. He closed his eyes, then opened them again; but it was still the same. He felt as if he was in a trance.

'It's just a dream', he thought, 'Yes, I'm not here at all. I'm at home in bed'.

Then, he suddenly came out of the trance and realized that he was really in school. The reality hit his mind like a ton of bricks. He panicked and ran to the school gates. He had to scramble over them in order to try and get home, which was the only place he wanted to be.

Once outside the school gates he stopped to think. He buried his face in his hands and, in the darkness that they made, he could think clearly.

'I've got to get home', he thought desperately. 'Number 47 bus at the top of the road. It'll take me right home'.

Geoff took his hands away from his eyes, ran up to the bus stop and sat on the wall opposite it, shaking. The bus came, and Geoff got on and sat upstairs on the top deck. There was nobody except him. He felt a bit better as he closed his eyes and breathed in relief as well as air.

After this, Geoff was reluctant to return to school in case the dizziness came back. The School Inspector didn't make it any easier for him.

'Well Geoff', he said, 'You've still got a couple of days left this week to go to school. Why don't you go in tomorrow?'

This terrified Geoff, and he insisted on staying home for 'one more day'.

'I'll start properly on Monday', he said.

But there was no escaping from the fact that he just had to attend school. He managed to prevent the School Inspector coming round to his house by going to school a day here and there. But whatever he did, he was always very depressed.

After a while the attacks of dizziness grew so bad that the school doctor suggested that he should wear spectacles. If it was to make him better, Geoff would try anything! He was issued with a pair of National Health spectacles which seemed to be curing him—until one day when he was kicked in the eye by a boy he was fighting with. He was taken to a nearby hospital where his eye was treated.

After this, Geoff's hopes of ever getting to like the school had evaporated. And as he made his way across the playground he had no idea that in two weeks, after an interview with the headmaster of Northwall Secondary School, he would be transferred.

Northwall was much nearer home for Geoff than Elgan. After a time he seemed to be settling down and feeling more at ease with himself. He attended school regularly for about three months until he was made to stay at home because of 'flu. While he was ill, school was completely shut out of his thoughts and his life, and when he got better, he couldn't face the thought of school. The dizzy spells came back, even though he wore spectacles. He also sometimes had attacks of being short of breath. He developed agoraphobia, so he was too terrified to step out of the house for fear he would stop breathing and die. He had to stay at home to be safe inside the shell which was to take the place of Stanford Primary School. He did not want the shell to open.

The psychiatrist's office was on the second floor of a London hospital. Geoff sat down on a seat outside the room where his mother was talking to the doctor. It was a comfortable place. Facing the stairs was a playroom which was scattered with toys and games. Stacks of comics and books occupied one corner of the room, which was decorated with colourful wallpaper. Geoff was sitting on a red seat which stretched the whole length of the wall. He was looking at the name that was printed on the frosted window of the door; 'Dr Barnes', it read. Underneath were lots of smaller letters which Geoff didn't have time to read, because suddenly the door swung open.

'The doctor wants to see you', said Geoff's mother.

Geoff got up slowly and went in.

'Hello Geoff', said a woman who was sitting behind a desk. 'Come and sit down'.

Geoff was really surprised to find that the psychiatrist was a woman. He was always under the impression that psychiatrists were men.

It was a friendly looking room. Small colourful pictures blended well with the bright wallpaper.

'Now Geoff', said Dr Barnes, picking up a folder from her desk. 'You have been sent here, as are a lot of children, because you have a few problems. Well remember, I am here to help you. If you have anything bothering you, or you want to speak to someone, don't hesitate to come to me. You won't have to come regularly. Some children only come once a week, once a fortnight or just a day here and there. It depends on how they're improving'.

Geoff nodded.

'Now I have a question to ask you Geoff', Dr Barnes continued. 'Why don't you want to go to school?'

Geoff told her of his dizzy spells. She listened with interest.

'And do you know what brings on these dizzy spells?'

'I don't know', said Geoff.

'And you only feel at ease when you're at home—am I right?'

'Yes'.

'Don't you ever get bored?'

'No'.

'What do you do at home?'

'Cooking', answered Geoff. 'And then there's the telly. I paint and I help my Mum do the housework, if I'm not doing my bike'.

'Do you go out on your bike?'

'Only round the block. I can't go any further, 'case I get a bit frightened'.

'Frightened? Frightened of what?' asked the doctor.

'I don't know', mumbled Geoff, feeling a bit uncomfortable. The doctor wrote something in her folder.

'Do you watch a lot of television?'

'Yes, quite a bit'.

'Do you watch the school programmes?' came the next question.

'Sometimes'.

The doctor closed the folder.

'You can go home now', she said. 'And in the next two weeks I want you to try and get out as much as you can. Ride around on your bike. Go for walks. And, also, and this is most important, watch as many school programmes as you can'.

She got up and opened the door for Geoff; 'And remember to wear your glasses'.

Then Geoff's mother was called in.

'Make an appointment for two weeks' time', the doctor said to Geoff, holding the door open. 'The secretary's in the little room at the end of the corridor'.

Geoff got up and started to walk towards the secretary's room. The doctor called him back, 'I'll get in touch with the School Inspector', she said, 'So you won't be hearing from him again'.

Geoff saw the doctor again two weeks later, and was told he could stay at home for another two weeks in which Geoff never once attended school. In that time he showed rapid improvement. His dizziness had completely stopped, and he felt far more confident when leaving his house. So it came as no surprise to Geoff to learn that he was to see the psychiatrist for the last time.

'The thing is Geoff', said the doctor, 'even though you're more at ease, you're not really learning anything apart from the things you see on the schools' programmes. So therefore, I think it would be best if you went to a tutorial class'.

Geoff nodded. He could just imagine all his troubles starting again.

'What's a tutorial class?' he asked half-heartedly.

'It's nothing like school', said the doctor reassuring him. 'It's a place where you go to take your mind off school, yet it gives you the education you so badly need. There will be other children there with problems like yourself. You will only have to go for four mornings a week. And that can't be bad! How about giving it a try?'

The Monday after, Geoff was sitting in front of a plump but friendly lady in the tutorial class.

'Well did you get here all right?' asked Mrs Cox, the teacher of the tutorial. She was a short woman, about five foot three inches tall. She had short black hair, pale blue eyes and a round face with very small features.

'I nearly didn't get here at all', answered Geoff.

'What happened?'

'I jumped on a bus. I had second thoughts about coming'.

'Oh I see. Would you like a cup of tea? Or maybe you would like a cup of coffee?'

'No thanks', said Geoff.

Whenever he was nervous he could never eat or drink.

'You were saying, you jumped on a bus', said Mrs Cox looking up from making her coffee.

'Well', said Geoff, 'I got on the bus and I was having second thoughts about coming here', he repeated. 'I walked down the street and stopped outside the class and I was trying to pull myself into the class. But I couldn't. It was like there were two people inside me. One was saying, 'Don't go in. Stay at home, you'll be safe there'. And the other was saying, 'Take no notice of that idiot. You go in the class. After all it's the best thing to do'. I stopped and thought about it and I decided to give it a try and come in. And well, here I am'.

Mrs Cox looked at Geoff. 'Well Geoff', she said, 'if your little friends ever come back, bring them in here with you and we'll give them a cup of tea'.

They both laughed. Mrs Cox poured some fresh ground coffee from the percolator.

'You sure you won't have some?' she asked.

Geoff hesitated. 'Oh well, OK then', he said.

After they finished their coffee and biscuits, Mrs Cox showed him around.

'It's only a small place', she said, 'but it's big enough for the amount of children that come here in the mornings.'

'What about the afternoons?'

'They're much the same as the mornings, only there are more children. Six to be exact', said Mrs Cox, showing Geoff into the next room.

Geoff liked this place. It had a friendly atmosphere unlike the previous school he had been in.

'Have you ever worked in English work books?' Mrs Cox asked.

Geoff shook his head.

'Well they're books with the questions already in them and they leave little spaces for you to fill in the answers. It's quite fun. I sometimes have a go myself. Anyway, for an hour every day you'll work on this work book'.

She picked one up from the table.

'The rest of the day you've got free to paint, cook, or do some woodwork. And we've also got a record player. And if you like, you can play Scrabble'.

'What's Scrabble?' asked Geoff.

'You don't know what Scrabble is!' exclaimed Mrs Cox. 'You haven't lived! I tell you what, I'll give you a game later on'.

Later on Geoff was sitting opposite Mrs Cox for the second time that day. This time, instead of tea cups there was a Scrabble board on top of the desk. Geoff was sitting fiddling about with the small square plastic markers which the letters were written on.

'Vertigo!' shouted Mrs Cox as she placed the letters 'V.E.R.T.I' down on the board next to 'G.O'.

Geoff had found that the object of the game was to try and make up as many words as he could. Some letters had numbers on them. Geoff found out that the player with the highest number wins. Geoff had never been so bored with any game in his life as he was with Scrabble.

The next day Geoff managed to force himself into the class. In fact, he went regularly for two months. In that time he had painted fifteen pictures (one of them being a four foot by four foot mural of Trevor Brooking, scoring a goal for West-Ham from the penalty spot), baked forty cakes (burnt twelve), made a ship out of balsa wood, and made thirty-five cups of tea and fifty cups of coffee. But the most important achievement of all was that he had only one dizzy spell in the whole of the two-month period. Things were definitely looking up for Geoff.

It was coming to the end of another coffee-making, picture-painting, model-constructing day. The smaller children (three of them) were in the painting room painting some pictures. Geoff was in the main room where Mrs Cox was talking to a lady about her son. From what Geoff could gather, the lady's son had much the same trouble as himself.

'Poor Sod', thought Geoff, 'I know how he feels'.

Mrs Cox called Geoff over.

'Would you like to do me a favour?' she asked.

'What is it?'

'Well this lady's son, David has had the same trouble with school as you. Well, more or less. And he's a bit reluctant to come. So I think if you went around to his house on your way here tomorrow, you'd probably be able to get him to come'.

'What's his address?' asked Geoff.

'It's seventy-eight Little Turner Street', said the lady.

'All right', said Geoff. 'I'll call for him at half-past nine then'.

Having drunk the last of her coffee, the lady thanked Geoff, shook hands with Mrs Cox and left.

'What's her name?' asked Geoff, turning to Mrs Cox.

'Mrs Cook, to you', she said smiling.

'She didn't say much, did she?' said Geoff.

'Perhaps it was the coffee', remarked Mrs Cox, as she lifted the cup with a grin.

CHAPTER 2

SCHOOL PHOBIA

The sleek black cat jumped lightly onto the chair. It rolled over onto its back and purred contentedly. The thin, dark-haired boy looked at it from across the kitchen table.

'I wish I was a cat', David said, 'then I wouldn't have to go to school and I could laze around all day or do whatever I wanted to'. all day or do whatever I wanted to.'

'Go to school,' he thought, and shuddered.

'The problem is,' he said out loud again, "I'm not a cat and have to go to school.'

'But why must children be forced to go to school, whether they like it or not,' he thought. 'That's the trouble with the world today, people are forced to do too many things; they don't always realise it, but it happens all the time. Take me, for instance,' he went on, 'here I am sitting in the kitchen talking to the cat like a nut, while my mum's gone to some mad house called a tutorial class to see if they've got a place for me there. All because the Council says I have to go to some place where I can be educated. Why should some bunch of old twits be worried about me. If I had gone to the secondary school I wanted to go to, I probably wouldn't be in the mess I'm in now. It was all because of that bloody headmaster I had at my Primary School. Yes, it was all because of him.'

He could remember it well. He was in the headmaster's office with his father having the interview that every child has before leaving Primary School. The reason for the interview was to give the headmaster an idea of the school his pupil would like to go to, and to decide whether this school was suitable. And it also gave both or one of the parents a chance to express their views on the subject.

'Well, that's fair enough,' David Cook had thought.

But things don't always work out that way. He had told the headmaster where he wanted to go, (his brother Stephen's school), but the headmaster had replied,

'I don't really think your other son's school is suitable for David, Mr. Cook, because —' he paused, 'being a grammar school, I don't think that David could keep up with the other boys.'

Of course, his father had agreed, and with a lot of talking from both parties, (but not from himself) they finally put his name down for his older brother Paul's school. This was a massive Comprehensive School with one thousand, nine hundred boys, to David, all seven feet tall.

'And that's when all the trouble began,' he went on.

He could remember the first day clearly. He remembered walking towards the big black iron gates, and into the much bigger playground. He was nervous, but not terrified, at that stage. There seemed to be millions of uniforms everywhere, and so much noise. He had never heard anything like it in his life.

A prefect stopped him as he was walking across the playground.

'Are you a first year?' he asked.

'Yes,' replied David.

The prefect pointed across the playground at a small square building.

'You see that building over there?' he said.

David nodded.

"Well, that's the gym. Go over there and line up with all the other first years, and then somebody will come along and organise you and tell you where you've got to go. All right?'

'All right', said David.

He walked across the playground and stood at the back of a rather noisy queue until two more prefects and a teacher came along. The teacher faced the queue and waited until all the talking had stopped. He looked down at the pale green register in his hand.

'Right, let's see whether you're all here, shall we?' he said loudly, sounding much like a sergeant addressing a group of new recruits.

After the teacher had checked everybody's name, he led them into a large assembly hall. David and the other boys were made to sit in the front rows. The headmaster came in accompanied by six other teachers. He started to give a lecture on why school days are the best days of one's life. And he said in a loud dramatic voice that he would not tolerate any fighting or bullying or violence of any kind, and that if there were any problems, everybody should go to see him. (But nobody ever did − they were all far too frightened of him.)

The headmaster finished his lecture and walked out of the hall. The youngest-looking one of the six teachers strode over to a stack of chairs leaning against the wall in the corner. He lifted the top one off, took it back to the very same spot where the headmaster had been standing, put it down and sat on it.

'The other five teachers and myself are your form masters. After I've told you all what form you're going to be in, you'll be taken to the main block by your form master and shown where your form room is.'

David's form room was on the sixth floor and was reached by a gigantic lift followed by a walk through what seemed like an endless series of long corridors. David, with the other boys in his class, spent most of the first day here copying down the timetable, being given various books, and learning where everything was.

For the following weeks David seemed to be settling down and the noise and bustle of the school didn't bother him at first. But one day, as he approached the school gates, he could not bear the thought of another day of being bullied, pushed and shoved on the crowded stairs. So, instead of going through the gates, he walked round the corner and managed to catch a bus that was pulling away from the bus stop. Sitting on the upstairs deck of the bus, he was in a trance. He could not believe what he had done.

'I've never played truant in my life,' he said to himself. 'Oh well,' he thought, 'tomorrow I'll go in and say I was ill or something. I won't play truant any more.'

But he did. He didn't go to school the next day. In fact, he didn't go for the following two weeks. He would set out for school from home in the morning, wait for the bus to come and then, when all the other boys got off at the bus stop outside the school, David would stay on for another four or five stops, then get off and walk about all day. He would have no money or food, and sometimes he would sit on a park bench in some deserted spot and stay there for hours, just thinking of the terrible thing he had done. After a while his fear of school grew so bad that he would try almost anything to stay away.

On one occasion he recalled he had not managed to stay on the bus after all the other boys had got off because a prefect had been sitting next to him. So after assembly he asked his form master if he could go to the lavatory. The teacher said he could. As the lavatory was situated right next to the gate David had no trouble in climbing over the top and getting out of school. Once outside, he ran as fast as he could, in case a teacher or prefect saw him. It was a cold October morning and it was very foggy so the chances of anybody seeing him were slim; that is, if they were across the road; but not if they were as close as the teacher that David ran straight into as he rushed round the corner into the main road. He looked up and saw it was the P.E. teacher. David's thoughts started racing. What would he do? Run? No! Being the P.E. teacher he would have no trouble in catching David. Then David thought of something to say.

'It's the fog! I can't find the school!'

It was a feeble excuse but the teacher seemed to believe it.

'Oh, I see,' he said, 'well you'd better follow me then.'

David followed him round the corner. Suddenly he had an idea.

'The fog,' he thought, 'yes, the fog.' He realised that the only way to get away now was to get further and further away from the teacher until he could not be seen. He wouldn't have to go far as the fog was very thick. The teacher was in front of him, and he was walking very fast. David slowed down his pace so that he was about five feet behind the teacher, then ten feet, then fifteen feet, then he could no longer see him. David ran as fast as he could for the second time that morning, and for the second time as he got further and further away from the school, he told himself to stop pissing around and go back. But like everybody else, David had two sides to him; a side that thought logically and a side that thought illogically. Every day the illogical side of him won, and that was the side that told him to run at the slightest opportunity.

After about three weeks, David's mother found out that he was not attending school. So she realised that the only way to get him there was to take him.

He recalled one occasion when he and his mother were walking to school. They turned the corner and were facing it and all David could think about as they got closer and closer were those big black iron gates, and the thought of being behind them like a prisoner. To him the whole school was a prison. He was trapped, every time he was behind those gates. He was like a bird locked in a cupboard and he reacted in the same way. All this raced through his mind as he approached those big black iron gates and the glass cells. Then his mind went blank, except for one thought. And that was to get away, to escape.

He could still remember his mother screaming, 'Come back,' and he could still feel his heart racing. It seemed as if he ran for ever that terrible day.

There was another occasion that David would never ever forget. He had slipped out of the school shortly after lunch. His cousin, who also went to the school, had gone with him. David, knowing he would get into even more trouble if he took someone else with him when he played truant, thought up an excuse to get rid of his cousin.

'I'm just going home to get my door key', he said, 'or I

won't be able to get in after school. I would have brought it this morning only I forgot it'.

His cousin believed him and went back to school.

David had it all planned out. There was only one lesson that he did not have much trouble in forcing himself to go to, and that was history. He had got his attendance mark at lunch time, so if he got back in time for history (which was just after break at three o'clock), he probably would not be found out. And also he would at least be able to tell himself that he nearly stayed in school for the whole day.

He spent the afternoon sitting in a park about two miles away from the school. At half-past two, he started to make his way back. He arrived at the school at 2.55 but he could not see anybody making their way back to classes. He wondered what had happened. If the bell had rung then it could only have gone a few seconds before David had arrived. But even then all one thousand, nine hundred boys would not suddenly have rushed to their classrooms as if a third world war had broken out.

David was very perplexed as he walked up the stairs towards the history room. He went along the corridor and opened the classroom door. He was stunned! What could have happened! There, facing the teacher were forty boys sitting behind their desks copying something from the blackboard. They all looked up as David opened the door.

'And where have you been, pray tell?' said the teacher sarcastically.

'I've been home to get my door key', answered David.

'Why?' asked the teacher sharply.

'Because I can't get in without it'.

The whole form started laughing. David's excuse was not very good. He had not been prepared for this so the only thing he could do was mumble.

'That was not a very good answer' said the teacher. 'Shall we try again? Now, why did you go home?'

David had never felt so small and helpless in all his life. What could he say?

'I think', said the teacher, 'we had better go downstairs and then you can explain it to the headmaster and see what he thinks'.

David followed the history teacher downstairs and into the headmaster's office.

The headmaster's secretary nodded when the history teacher asked if he could go straight in. David followed and stood looking down at his shoes.

'I was sitting upstairs in my class teaching this lad's form, and all of a sudden the wanderer returned'.

'Oh yes', said the headmaster looking at David. 'This one does make a habit of touring London when he should be in school'.

He got up and walked round his desk and stood in front of David with his hands in his pocket.

'What's his excuse this time?' he asked the history teacher without taking his eyes off David.

'He says he had to go home to get his door key. He also said that he told his cousin to come and tell me that he might be a bit late. He said that he had permission from you'.

'Oh yes', said the headmaster to David, 'that's a right load of rubbish, isn't it?'

'Yes' said David in a low voice.

The headmaster walked over to a high glass-fronted cabinet. He opened it, took out one of the seven or eight canes that hung on little hooks, and walked back to David. He hit the cane on the table with a loud 'whack' to test it. He turned to David.

'You are Paul Cook's brother, aren't you' he said.

'Yes'.

The headmaster looked at the history teacher. 'Paul Cook, he was a bit funny as well you know'.

'Don't say it runs in the family', said the teacher.

'Unfortunately it does', said the headmaster.

He turned to David. 'I have just about had enough of you'. he said loudly. 'You've been running away ever since you've been in this school. Your mother has even brought you, but you still insist on playing truant. Well, let's see if you still play truant after a good whacking. Now bend over and touch your toes'.

David bent over. The cane gave a loud thud as it hit him. He would always remember that caning. The feeling of injustice had never left him and he doubted if it ever would. But a lot had happened since then. He had been to two schools and had not settled in either of them.

The first was a private boarding school called Wallington College in Berkshire. A man from the ILEA had come to David's house and said that perhaps David would be better off at a boarding school. He showed David and his mother some leaflets and they decided to try for Wallington College. About a week later, a letter came back from the school saying that David should come down with his parents to have an interview on April 12th. He was taken down there by his father. (His mother had to look after his little sister).

There were two schools in the grounds. The prep school for children up to the age of thirteen and the senior school for children over thirteen and up to college age. So there were two headmasters. David and his father were led into the senior headmaster's office. They talked for about an hour and then David was taken into another room where he was given an exam. While he was doing this his father was shown round the school grounds.

A few days later a letter came saying that David had been accepted because he had passed the entrance exam.

He was taken to the school by his father and his two brothers. They drove down a long drive and parked the car in the quad. In the centre was a small grass roundabout with the flags of the various countries on high flag poles. The flags were in a circle in the middle of the roundabout. David, his father and his two brothers walked down a long concrete path that led from the quad to the main entrance of the school. A young boy of about eleven came up to them and told them that they should go to one of the teachers and find out what dormitory David was in. They found a teacher, who showed them up a wide staircase, along a narrow corridor, and into one of the dormitories. It was a large room with five beds against the wall on the left as you came in. Against the opposite wall was the same number of chests of drawers. Fixed onto the wall above them was a long mirror stretching half the length of the wall. And right down at the other end of the room was a wide modern window overlooking the quad. This room, and in fact the whole school, was very modern and new. David liked the look of the place. But would he be able to settle down?

David's father said that he had to go as he had to get back to work. So David went down to the quad with him to say good-bye and see them off. After that, he came back to see what he was to do next. It was 4.15 so the school was going to have tea. David followed the other boys into a large dining hall. Tables were set out in long lines the whole length of the hall. At the far end of the hall was a raised platform. It was much like a stage David thought. On the platform was a long table where the teachers ate. At the top of the table sat the headmaster.

The seating in the rest of the hall was a copy of this. At the top of every table sat a form prefect. Every table had six seats round it so every form had three tables. Tea lasted for about three quarters of an hour. After that, the headmaster said he wanted to see all the new boys in his office in ten minutes. David made his way there and was surprised to see that there were only twenty-five new boys. They were lined up outside the door. The headmaster opened the door and told them all to come in and sit down on the floor. It was a very comfortable room with a desk in the corner, several armchairs and a settee. David had a strange feeling of deja vu when the headmaster said he would not tolerate any fighting, bullying, or violence of any kind, and that if there were any problems everybody should go to see him.

After that, for the rest of the evening David and the other new boys unpacked and tried to find out where everything was. At half-past nine David was told to go to his dormitory and get ready for bed.

The next morning when David woke up, the stark reality of being in a school and being away from home hit him like a ton of bricks. When he was half awake he felt and thought he was at home. But when he finally woke up completely, he realised where he was; at school. But this time the sickening feeling of being locked in that normally came to him when he was in school, was much, much worse. This was because he was actually living in the school. He couldn't go home at night and forget about it, and in the morning not go; for he was in the school the whole time. Every morning when he woke up he would find himself in that terrible place. He lived there. That was his home. He knew that at home he had a fairly good chance of playing truant, but here it was so much harder. All this raced through his mind as he sat up in his bed and looked round the room.

'Oh my God!' he thought, 'why did I come here?'

Just then he heard a bell ringing, then another and another, until the whole school was engulfed with the noise of ringing bells and prefects shouting 'Everybody up, everybody up'. David followed the other boys to the first of two bathrooms at the end of the corridor. After washing, they all went down to the dining room where they had breakfast. After that they went to the part of the school where the classrooms were.

At 12 o'clock after Maths and English David ran away from the boarding school for the first time. Dinner was served at half-past twelve so the boys spent the half hour beforehand playing football or just walking around the grounds. David decided to do the latter. He walked along a path leading to the farm that the school owned. Before he knew where he was, he was standing at the corner of the London road; it was then that he decided to run away from the school and get home. He stepped on the grass verge next to the road and thought. It was a very long way to London and he had no money or food. But David's fear of school was much stronger than logical thinking and he was determined to get home whatever the cost.

He decided to go to the nearest British Rail station where he hoped he might be able to make the man in the ticket office believe that he was lost after being left behind at an outing that he went on with a London school. He desperately hoped they would believe him, and take down his name and address so that they could send for the fare money from his parents, and let him go to London for nothing. He started walking towards Oxford which was about ten miles from the school. Ten miles is a long way for a twelve-year-old boy to walk, but David's fear kept him going.

He walked for about an hour, following the signs at the side of the road. He was very cold as it was the end of October but he still kept on walking. All of a sudden a blue Viva slowed down and pulled into the verge about thirty feet in front of David. David panicked. Who was it? A teacher? A policeman? He did the only thing he could think of: he turned round and walked away in the opposite direction. Whoever it was, might change their mind.

'Christ! What shall I do? Whoever it is, go away and leave me alone. Please go away!'

He looked across the road. The blue Viva was going at the same speed as David. He recognised the driver. It was Thompson, the music teacher. He wound the window down.

'Wait there', he shouted across to David.

The car waited until the road was clear and swung over to David.

'Hullo David' said a voice behind him.

He turned around. It was Mr Riley, the Maths Teacher. David hadn't realised that there were two men in the car.

'Mr Riley must have got out before Mr Thompson turned the car round', he thought. 'They must be used to this. One person walking in case I decided to double back. And another in a car in case I decided to run. Yes, they have definitely done this before'.

Mr Thompson opened the door for David. He pushed the front passenger seat forward and held it there as David got in and sat down at the back. Mr Riley sat down in the front next to Mr Thompson and slammed the door shut. The car pulled away from the side of the road and drove back towards the school. Mr Riley turned to David.

'Where were you going?' he asked.

'Home', came the reply.

'Home for you is over fifty miles away? Did you know that?'

'Yes'.

'Well, how do you propose to get there'.

'I was going to walk'.

David thought that it was best that he did not tell anyone of his plan to bluff British Rail as then a station would be the first place they would look for him when he ran away again. Both men started laughing at his last remark.

'Apart from the fact that you have probably never walked fifty miles in your life, you would never be able to walk home because the police don't like little boys walking about the countryside on their own. Look', continued Mr Riley in more serious tones, 'we all like to get away now and again but we can't just get up and go whenever we like. Stay in school. It's not that bad'.

They turned the corner of the school drive.

'If you want to get out', said Mr Thompson grinning, 'wait until we have a school outing'.

They parked the car in the grounds and walked into the school. Mr Riley told David to sit on one of the chairs that was outside the headmaster's office. He walked over to Mr Thompson said something and walked down the corridor in the direction of the staff room. Mr Thompson knocked on the door of the office and walked in. A couple of seconds later he came out and told David to go inside.

David stepped into the room. Mr Thompson shut the door and walked down the corridor. The headmaster was sitting at his desk writing something. Without looking up, he told David to sit down. There was silence except for the scratching of the headmaster's pen. Then he sat up straight, put the top of his pen back on, closed the book he was writing in and came and sat down next to David.

'Now then, what's all this silliness about?' he asked in the tone of a vicar talking to his congregation.

David didn't answer. He just sat there with his head bowed.

'You know', the headmaster went on, 'when I was a boy I had more or less the same trouble as you. I couldn't stand being in school. I'd much rather have been at home reading a comic and eating chocolate. But of course when I played truant I couldn't possibly go home in case I got a good spanking. So instead, I went fishing with a friend at a nearby river. Yes, those were the days. We used to sit for hours holding our home-made fishing rods, sticks with pieces of string tied on them! Mind you, we couldn't afford to buy proper bait so we had to make do with the flies we caught'.

It sounded more like Tom Sawyer than a real-life happening, David thought.

'But we were soon found out', said the headmaster, 'and I got the worst spanking of my life', he chuckled, 'I couldn't sit down for a week'. Then his voice went serious. 'Of course, I can't spank you, so it is entirely up to you whether you are going to settle down. Think of your parents. They were worried sick when I had to phone them up and tell them that you were missing. And also think of yourself. Great harm can come to you if you walk about the countryside on your own.' He got up. 'Go to your dormitory now'.

David got up and walked to the door. 'Thank you Sir', he said.

'It would be pretty bad if I couldn't help my own pupils'. He walked to his desk. 'And remember what I've told you'.

David walked out and shut the door behind him. He went up to the dormitory and lay down on his bed with his hands behind his head. There was no-one about; everyone was either down in the library or outside in the grounds. He lay there reflecting on the one-sided conversation in the headmaster's office. He liked the headmaster. He was friendly and kind, but when it came to dealing with boys who had a fear of school and didn't go fishing when they played truant, he had as much idea as flying in the sky. All the talking he had done had fallen on deaf ears because he had not put David at ease—in fact, David was even more determined to get home.

At six o'clock the boys came upstairs to the dormitory to wash their hands and get ready for dinner. The four other boys in David's dormitory came in and found him reading a book. Richard Carr, the eldest one, stood at the end of David's bed.

'Well, well, well', he said, 'Look who's here'.

He walked up and snatched the book away from David. He looked at him and sneered. 'Come to visit us, have you? Where did you go this afternoon?'

'I went for a walk', said David, taking the book back.

'You went for a very long walk. The grape vine says you were trying to get home. Big baby! Want your mummy, do you?' He turned over to the chest of drawers opposite his bed and took out a shirt. He turned back to David. 'Well, let me tell you one thing. I for one don't want anything to do with you. I don't like babies'. He put his blazer on and walked out of the room with the other boys.

David got up and walked over to the chest of drawers at the bottom of his bed. He pulled out a clean white shirt and started to put it on. 'He's the big baby', he thought, 'just because I didn't get the cane, or told off by the headmaster, he's jealous'. He put on his blazer and made his way down to the dining hall and queued up with the other boys.

'Have a nice walk, did you?' said one of them. 'He only goes wandering about on his own because he's hoping to get raped'. They all laughed. All through dinner David received very nasty looks from everyone.

The following morning after football practice, David had his second chance to get home. All the boys were getting changed when David noticed that the door leading to the games field could not be seen from any part of the school. You could only see it if you were actually standing in the field. He decided that if he could run out of the door but stay parallel with the wall, he could cross the field and climb over the fence without being seen. He made his plan. The next day when all the boys were in their classes, he would make some excuse to get out and come to this part of the school.

The following day David made his way to the classroom block with the other boys. About an hour later he put up his hand and asked if he could go to the lavatory. The teacher said he could so David got up and walked out of the room. This was his chance! He went along the corridor towards the door that led out to the games field. There was no-one about as he opened the door.

'Thank God', he thought, 'Nobody's going to bring me back today. This time I'm really going to get home. And I'm not coming back'.

He looked out to see if anybody was about. All was clear. David opened the door wide and ran as fast as he could across the field making sure he kept parallel with the wall. He reached the low fence at the end of the field and jumped over it.

'At last I've done it! I've got out! Now to get home!'

He realised it would be madness to try to get to Oxford to catch a train as that would be the first place they would look when they found he was missing. So he decided to see if there was a station in the nearby village of Wallington. He walked for about a mile until he came to a small bookshop on the outskirts of the village. He went in and asked if there was a station nearby. The woman behind the counter told him that there wasn't a station in Wallington, but if he wanted to he could get a bus outside the Town Hall and it would take him to the station of a neighbouring village. After being directed to the Town Hall, David sat outside for half-an-hour until the bus came along. Every Saturday the school gave the boys twenty pence pocket money so David had enough money to pay the bus fare. But he did not have enough money for the fare to London. It was entirely up to fate and luck (and also if British Rail would believe his story). He paid his fare, walked to the back of the bus and sat down. He looked out of the window at the cars and shops.

What was he doing? Running away from school. It was like something out of Colditz. He felt like an escaped prisoner.

'Well, maybe that's what I am', he thought, 'but what am I a prisoner of? The school or myself? Who am I running away from? The school or myself?'

He sat there reflecting on the happenings of the past few days. What was this terrible fear? What was this phobia that stopped him from doing anything without running away? What the hell was happening? His thoughts were interrupted by the sharp brakes of the bus. He fell forward slightly as the bus stopped. Only three other passengers got off with him at the stop outside the station, a young man of about thirty, a middle-aged man and a middle-aged woman.

David followed the sign saying 'Station'. He walked down a long quiet road until he came to an old dusty railway station. This was the moment he had feared all along. He stood outside and thought. What should he do? Go back? He thought about school and a sickening fear ran through him. There was nothing to be frightened of in the station. They could only stop him from getting on a train. They couldn't send him back to the school. He walked up to the ticket office.

'Can I help you?' asked the old man through the small glass window.

'Well you see', said David nervously, 'I came down here on an outing with my school and I got lost'.

'Oh yes', said the man in a not-too-believing voice.

'And I wondered', went on David, 'if, seeing as I've got no money, you could let me get a train to London. I'll give you my name and address and you can send for the fare from my parents'.

The man looked David up and down. 'All right', he said, 'But the train doesn't leave until 11 o'clock, so you'd better wait in here'. He opened the door and David went in and sat down. The man turned to him and said, 'I've just got to go round to the back for a minute. You'll be all right on your own, won't you?'

'Yes'.

A few minutes later the door was opened by a young man of about twenty-eight with short black hair. He was wearing a blue shirt and a black tie. On top, he wore a dark blue coat. He was also wearing black trousers and black boots. David knew immediately that the man was a policeman. He walked over and looked down at David. The old man came in and stood behind him.

'Hello son', said the policeman. 'Thinking of going somewhere'.

'Yes, I got lost. I came on an outing with a school from London, but I missed the coach back'.

The policeman looked at the badge on David's blazer.

'Don't kid me son'. he said. 'I know where you come from. Wallington College, don't you?'

'Yes', said David slowly, 'I do'.

'Come on', said the policeman,' I'll get someone to take you back'.

David nearly fainted. 'Oh no', he thought, 'Not back to that school again'.

The policeman took him round the corner and they waited 'til a patrol car came to collect David. As the patrol car turned into the quad, David had never felt so bad in his life. He had tried to get home twice. And twice he had been brought back. How many more times must he run away before he could get home?

David walked into the school with the policeman. The policeman spoke with the headmaster for a few minutes in his office, then he came out and told David to go in.

David went through the same old one-sided conversation, only this time the headmaster talked for much longer. He seemed determined to talk David into liking the school. But his conversation again proved to be in vain.

The very next day David ran away again. He ran out of the same door after managing to slip away before the classes started. This time he tried to get to Oxford again. He walked along the side of the road for about two hours. Suddenly a car slowed down and stopped just in front of him.

'It's one of the teachers', thought David. But it wasn't. He had never seen the man that got out and walked towards him in his life.

'Do you go to Wallington College?' he asked as he came up to David.

'Yes'.

'Where are you going?'

'To Oxford to visit my aunt', answered David.

'Does the headmaster know where you're going?'

'Yes, I got his permission', said David.

'You see', said the man, 'my name is Mr Burgess and my son goes to your school. I've met the headmaster and he doesn't seem the type of man who would let his pupils go walking about the countryside on their own'.

'Well, he let me', said David.

'Shall we go and check on that?' said Mr Burgess.

'OK'.

They got into the car and drove to a phone box about half a mile away. Mr Burgess stopped the car on the other side of the road opposite the phone box.

'Wait here while I go and phone the headmaster. I shan't be a minute'.

He got out of the car and shut the door after him. David watched as he opened the door of the telephone box. He lifted up the receiver and dialled. He held the telephone under his chin, put some money in the slot, and started talking. David realised that Mr Burgess would find out the truth in a matter of minutes. He panicked.

'I'm not going to be taken back again. My only chance is to run'.

He opened the car door and ran down the narrow street. Mr Burgess saw David running and rushed out of the phone booth.

'Come back', he shouted.

David kept running. He noticed a small pub, and ran into it. There were only three people inside, the landlady and two old men. David was pretty sure that Mr Burgess hadn't seen him run into the pub so he decided to try and stay there for as long as he could, hoping that Mr Burgess would give up trying to find him. The landlady and the two old men looked at him as he came running through the door. David thought of something to say.

'Can I have a coke please?' he asked.

He had no money but he just had to bluff his way through the whole thing. The landlady looked him up and down. She took a bottle of Coca-Cola from the shelf behind her. She opened it, poured it into a glass and handed it to David. He took it and sat down on a chair, out of sight from the door. As he looked through the window of the pub, he saw Mr Burgess get out of his car and walk across the road towards the pub. David got up and looked round the room to see if there was another way out, but it was too late! Mr Burgess came in. At first he did not see David. He walked over to the landlady.

'Have you seen a young boy about?'

Suddenly he stopped. He had seen David.

'Come on, don't be silly', he said, 'Come back to the school. Come on'.

Mr Burgess paid the landlady for David's drink and they both went out and got into the car. They drove back to the school where David again had a talk with the headmaster. The headmaster seemed determined not to give in to David and let him go home. And David seemed determined to keep running away.

After another eight days of finding David after he had run away, the headmaster realised that something had to be done. So he telephoned David's parents and asked them to come down and see if they could suggest anything.

The next day, David found himself sitting in the headmaster's office with his parents and discussing his future at the school. After three hours of talking the headmaster reluctantly let David leave his school. David thanked him and apologised for all the trouble he had caused. He went up to the dormitory and packed his things. He had done it! He was going home. But had he achieved anything? What was he going to do now?

That night David's mother and father decided to make an appointment for him to see a child psychiatrist.

Three weeks later David found himself sitting in front of a tall white-haired man of about fifty-seven. This was the psychiatrist, Dr Chambers.

'Why are you here? Do you think you can tell me, David?'

'Well', said David, 'I'll try'.

'Go on,' said the doctor pulling a pen and note pad towards him. 'Don't be shy. You can tell me whatever you want.'

David talked for about twenty minutes. He told the doctor about the terrible feeling he had every time he was in a school. The doctor listened patiently. He occasionally asked a question and wrote something down on his pad. After this, David was taken to a room at the top of the hospital by an attractive young woman, where he spent more than an hour having an I.Q. test. He had never had such a strange test in his life. He felt that some questions needed a computer to answer them, while others were so simple that a baby would know the answer.

After the I.Q. test David went in and spoke to the psychiatrist again. The doctor looked at him.

'Your problem,' he said, 'is that you have an uncontrollable fear of school – a phobia. A phobia is an unreasonable fear and what I mean by 'unreasonable' is that normally the thing the person fears most is quite harmless. It could be a bird, or a mouse, or being in a lift, or on a high building. In your case it is being in school. So you are suffering from school phobia. But don't worry, I'm here to help you overcome your fear. Now the first thing we must do is to find you another school.'

David shuddered.

'I know how you feel,' said Dr. Chambers, 'but the only way you can beat your fear is to live with it. It will be hard, but you'll have to face it. After a while your fear will just disappear and you'll forget you ever had it. Now you've always wanted to go to your brother's school. Is that true?'

'Yes.' David's spirits rose. Perhaps he could be happy there.

'Well,' said the doctor, 'I'll try to arrange for you and your father to have an interview there. Would you like that?'

'Yes,' said David.

Two weeks later David's father received a letter saying that he and David should come to the school for an interview the following Monday.

David could tell at the interview that the headmaster did not really want him there. But he finally gave in after arguing about David's school record and accepted him.

In the first week at school David ran away twice. Why did he do it? He just didn't know. He would be walking towards the gates and suddenly, on impulse, he would run to the bus stop and jump on a bus. Perhaps it was out of habit, or perhaps it was the dark depressing atmosphere of the school that made him run away. David didn't know and he doubted if he ever would.

But after the first week David went regularly for about five weeks, and it seemed for a while that his troubles were over. But he would still have to push himself into the school, and one morning, he did not seem to be able to do this, and he spent the day wandering about. When he arrived home that night, his father said,

'Now you've put your foot in it. You've got yourself chucked out of school, haven't you.'

David just broke down and cried and screamed on the stairs. His father told him that the headmaster had phoned and said he was going to expel David, and that David was in the room with him at the time. But David knew that this wasn't true. The headmaster just didn't want him there. (He found out later that the headmaster had not even bothered to put his name on the register).

The cat got off the chair and jumped onto his lap.

'I can just imagine what this tutorial group is going to be like,' he thought. 'I bet there's going to be a load of screaming mad kids, and what's more, I bet they send some great hairy geezer to get me.'

The cat purred. He looked down at it. 'You know,' he said, 'you really are lucky!'

CHAPTER 3

ELUDING HIS ESCORT

Geoff left home and made his way to David's house. He wasn't in a very friendly mood, because if there was one thing he could not stand, it was doing errands for people. One errand in particular, the one that entailed collecting someone new for the tutorial class.

'I mean,' he thought, 'supposing they've got a bleeding great dog, or this David, or whatever his name is, gets stroppy because he doesn't want to come with me to the class. If that happens then it's 'muggins me' that cops it. There's no peace for the wicked,' he said to himself as he turned down Newton Road. He thrust his hands in his pockets.

'I'll have to get myself a job,' he went on, 'because if I'm even going to hope to get a bird, I've got to get some decent clothes. I'll take a walk down Whitehill Market after class.'

He walked around the corner of Little Turner Street and knocked on the door of number seventy-eight. The door was opened by a boy about seventeen years old. He had short brown hair and greeted Geoff with a smile. 'This,' Geoff thought, 'must be David's brother'. Which was a good guess as that was exactly who he was.

You could see it was an old house, perhaps eighty or ninety years old. But it was well looked after, unlike some of the old houses Geoff knew. He was led up three flights of stairs and into the kitchen. At the table sat David nervously sipping his tea. Normally he would have had a big breakfast, but with the thought of school hanging over him, (or in this case, something like school), he could not stomach anything other than a cup of tea.

David was under the impression that whoever was going to collect him was going to be 6' 7", have muscles like ballast tanks and a scar from ear to ear. So he was very surprised to see before him a small boy about five feet tall and aged about fourteen years with a babyish face and long brown hair that flopped over his eyes like a shaggy sheep dog looking at him from the doorway.

'Hello,' said the boy, 'I'm Geoff. Mrs Cox, the teacher of the tutorial class sent me round to collect you and tell you a bit about it.'

Just then Mrs Cook came in, 'Go on,' she said, 'get a move on, you're not going to your death you know, so don't look so miserable.'

David and Geoff walked down the narrow stairs.

'Make sure you get him there,' shouted Mrs Cook from the kitchen. 'I don't want him wandering about all day.'

David slammed the door and the two boys walked round the corner. The bright sunlight shone down between the houses casting the boys' shadows along the road.

'You'll like it there,' said Geoff as they crossed over the road. 'I've done some terrific paintings while I've been there. You can do some too, if you like.'

'I'm not very good at painting,' said David.

'You don't have to be. You can do whatever you like. You can bake cakes or do woodwork, and we've also got a record player.'

Geoff turned round just in time to see David run round the corner.

'Come back!'

'Why did I ever agree to bring this kid?' thought Geoff as he ran after David.

David ignored Geoff's shouts and just kept on dodging in and out of the crowd.

'I'm not going there,' he said to himself. 'I don't want to be made to stay in a classroom ever again, and that kid's certainly not going to get me there. I must get away.' He saw a tall building across the road. 'Up there,' he thought, 'I'll lose him in the flats.' He ran over the road and started running up the stairs, all the time saying to himself, 'I'm not going there,' over and over again.

Geoff ran after him and reached the sixth floor just in time to see the oblong shape of white light and the top of David's head in the lift, descend out of sight. He gasped for breath and dashed down the stairs to the next floor where he again saw the light of the lift disappear downwards. He swore under what little breath he had left and ran down to the next landing. He followed it down to the ground floor where he caught David running toward the door that led out to the street. David ran out and Geoff chased him until David finally came to a stop. He was leaning up against a wall, breathing heavily from exhaustion, when Geoff came running up to him.

'Why don't you give it a try?' gasped Geoff. 'It's not as bad as you think. It's only for three hours, for fuck's sake. Three bloody hours!'

Geoff waited in the noise and bustle of the busy street for his answer.

'Well, I'm too tired to run any more, so I'll have to give it a try,' said David.

Geoff smiled. 'Come on then,' he said. 'Let's get going!'

The tutorial class was situated by the side of a primary school overlooking the nursery and playground. The class itself was on the first floor of a two-storey building. There was a swimming pool on the ground floor which the children from the primary school used. On the first floor was the tutorial class and right at the top on the second floor was a cookery class which the girls from a nearby girls' school used.

David and Geoff climbed the stairs and opened the door to the tutorial class. Mrs Cox, who was sitting in the main room (which was directly opposite the door) asked Geoff to make some coffee and called David over to her.

'Well, David,' she said, placing down a 'Woman's Own', 'I suppose you know why you're here?'

David nodded.

'During the past week,' she went on, 'I've been reading a report on you and it's quite some report! But have you any idea why you had to get away from school?'

'No,' said David, 'just knew I had to get away. The psychia-chiatrist called it 'school phobia'. I even tried to set fire to one of the schools,' he went on as Geoff came in with the coffee.

Mrs Cox was smiling. 'Tell me about it,' she said.

'Well,' said David, 'it was when I was at Wallington College. I thought if it were to close down for some reason everyone would have to go home. I was going to start it in the school lab; with all those test tubes full of corrosive chemicals it should have gone up like a puff of smoke.'

He paused and took a drop of coffee. 'Anyway, I bought some matches from a shop just outside the school and I waited until all the boys were in bed and all the teachers were having their supper, then I got out of bed, put on my dressing gown and slippers and sneaked downstairs with the matches. I had to be very quiet 'cos I had to go past the teachers' staff room. I finally reached the lab and I was just going to open the door when I heard voices coming towards me, so I ran down the corridor and up the staircase at the far end of the school, where I managed to get back to my dormitory without anybody noticing me.'

'Did you try to set fire to it again?' asked Mrs Cox.

'No,' said David, 'it was too much of a nerve-wracking experience and I thought I might get caught.'

Mrs Cox turned to Geoff. 'Hide the matches, Geoff,' she laughed; and so did David and Geoff, which brought three smaller children in to see what the joke was.

Mrs. Cox turned to Geoff and asked him to show David around.

'This is the painting room,' said Geoff as they walked into the next room. 'Well really you can do whatever you like, but we just call it that because we do most of our painting in here.'

He then took David into the next room which was much larger than the previous one. Nailed onto the walls were a small number of pictures painted by the children. In one corner stood a gas cooker, and next to that was a cabinet in which stood a series of pots and pans and other cooking utensils. On top of that stood some bags of flour, sugar, currants and baking powders. And two jars of strawberry jam. There were also two tables in the room which had no use as far as anybody could see except for being goals when a game of football was played if it was raining. The room opposite had two cupboards against the wall in which were kept paints, brushes, palettes and certain cleaning powders. In the corner stood a sink and table. The passage led from this room, past the painting room and the main room and into the cloakroom.

After settling down for a while, David decided to try his hand at baking some cakes. He needed some flour and sugar which they did not have. So he was sent upstairs to the cookery class to see if he could borrow some of theirs. He walked through the door and was greeted by twenty-five smiling girls all ready to put their tins in the oven. Feeling more at ease now, he marched boldly over to the teacher and asked her if he could borrow some flour and sugar. He was generously supplied and made his way downstairs where he told Geoff of his twenty-five lovely discoveries. This was a matter to pursue further, they both thought.

The morning wore on. David did some painting while he waited for his cakes to bake. Twelve-thirty came and everybody went their own way. David went home, but Geoff walked down to Whitehill Market asking at different stalls if they needed any help. It was one o'clock when he walked into Penright's Supermarket, where he was confronted with the manager, after asking for a job.

'How old are yer Sonny?' he said in a thick Irish accent.

'Fourteen,' replied Geoff.

The manager was about five feet eight inches tall. He was a rather thin man with big blue eyes that looked as if they were going to fall out whenever he blinked. 'What's yer name?' he asked.

'Geoffrey Moller,' said Geoff.

The manager smiled slightly. 'Moller, what kind of a name is that?' he asked.

Geoff didn't answer.

'Have yer done any shop work before?' enquired the manager whose name was 'Pitfield'.

'No,' said Geoff.

'Well, it's bloody hard work and I don't want yer rupturing yerself lifting stuff, but I'll give yer a try. When can yer start?'

'Right now,' said Geoff excitedly.

'Have yer left school?' asked Pitfield.

'No,' answered Geoff, 'I only go in the mornings. It's a special class.'

'Oh, I see,' said Pitfield.

Geoff was taken downstairs into the warehouse underneath the shop. He noticed two benches and on them were bacon cutting machines where some people were preparing trays for the front windows. Geoff was led to a conveyor belt where bags of flour and sugar were coming down. Paper, which had to be tidied up, stacked in large boxes and put out for the dustmen to collect, was also coming down the belt. The three men who had been struggling with big bags of sugar had left by the time Geoff had tidied up the paper. He later found out that they were from Tate and Lyle and that they were only moving the sugar about because there was no-one else to do it.

The manager came down and walked over to Geoff.

'Can yer tie a slip knot?' he asked, picking up a piece of string from the floor.

'No,' answered Geoff.

Mr Pitfield proceeded to show him how it was done.

'Yer see,' he said, 'yer get. about ten yards of string.' He measured a rough ten yards by getting hold of the string and stretching his arms out sideways. 'Now yer can double it up, or yer can just use it single,' he went on. 'When yer do it with the string double, yer place the string on the floor, and then yer put all the card that's been broken up like this.'

He demonstrated by picking up a box and opening the end after getting his finger caught on the sharp metal staples that held it together. After swearing and sucking his bleeding finger he threw the box on the floor and stamped on it.

'And that's how yer flatten the bloody thing!' he shouted.

By half-past-five Geoff had all the paper tidied up and put in boxes ready to be taken away by the dustman the next day. He had done a good job and he looked forward to seeing David and telling him all about it the following day.

CHAPTER 4

THIRD FLOOR OBJECTIVE

'Hello Geoff, come to collect David have you?' shouted Mrs Cook from the upstairs window of Seventy-eight Little Turner Street.

'Yes,' replied Geoff.

'Well, hang on a minute, he's just putting his jacket on.'

'He'd better hurry up,' thought Geoff, 'or we'll be late for class. It's half-past-nine already.'

David came out of the house and slammed the door behind him.

'Looks like we're in for another sunny day, don't it?' said Geoff, trying to make some idle chat. David just grunted and contrived to look at something across the road.

'Still feeling nervous?' asked Geoff, presuming that this was why David was looking so miserable.

'Yes,' replied David.

'Don't worry, you'll get used to it.'

'I hope I will,' came the reply.

They walked round to Newton Road.

'Hang on a minute' exclaimed Geoff, 'I haven't told you about my job yet, have I?'

'No, you haven't.'

'I don't have to do sod all *and* I get good money. It's really dead cushy, I tell yer!'

'Oh yer,' said David, not very enthusiastically.

'Blimey,' said Geoff, 'you look like you've just found out you've got the pox. Cheer up, it's not the end of the world. Look, I know it's hard forcing yourself to go to the class; I had to do the same thing. I mean it's not a bit like school. Now is it?'

'No, I suppose not,' said David slowly.

They were both outside the tutorial class by now and Geoff noticed the ice-cream van parked with the two right-hand wheels up on the pavement opposite the railings of the primary school.

'Do you wanna ice-lolly?' asked Geoff.

'I thought you were always out of money,' said David, cheered up by the thought of free refreshment.

'Not always,' said Geoff as he approached the van. 'Do you want one then?' he asked again.

'No thanks,' said David, 'but I'll have a drink if he's got any.'

'The only drinks I've got, son,' said the ice-cream man popping his head out of the window, 'are iced up and are on sticks.

They're called 'ice-lollies". He laughed at his own witty remark stopping abruptly when he saw that neither David nor Geoff raised even a polite smile.

'Can I have one then, please?' said Geoff, completely ignoring the ice-cream man's last remark.

Geoff was handed a lolly shaped, or supposed to be, like a space rocket. It was one of those multi-coloured affairs; red at the top, green in the middle and yellow at the bottom. On the wrapper was a picture of what looked like an astronaut eating the same lolly. At the top in bold red print were the words, 'Orbit Ice.'

'They get around these lollies, don't they!' laughed Geoff as he pointed to the astronauts.

They made their way across the playground toward the building where the tutorial class was held. All the children of Morton Primary School were in assembly, so the playground was empty except for David and Geoff.

'It's funny,' said David, more at ease now. 'How different the sun makes everything look. I mean,' he turned to Geoff, 'what would we be doing if it was raining?'

'Getting wet,' grinned Geoff.

'No,' continued David, 'if it was raining we would not be able to appreciate the beauty that the sun provides — like the flowers and....'

'Have you gone poof?' interrupted Geoff.

'Of course not' said David. 'I was just giving you an example.'

'Yeah, I know', laughed Geoff.

They walked up the stairs of the tutorial class. It was ten o'clock and the class would just be starting. They reached the second landing where they found two of the smaller children of the class standing outside the door.

'She's not here yet,' said Simon, the taller of the two in a very loud voice. It was not often that Mrs Cox was late. But for David and Geoff this was a blessing in disguise. They heard some footsteps coming up the stairs. Then voices. One of the voices said, 'Be careful, Val. Mind that flour.'

David, Geoff, Simon and John watched as two struggling girls carrying a heavy load of what looked like (from where David was standing) several bags of flour and sugar.

'Hang on a minute,' he shouted down to them, 'we'll give you a hand.'

The two girls looked up. They were both about fourteen years old. The smaller one had big blue eyes, a small nose and long brown hair which hung down nearly reaching her waist. She gave a smile when Geoff said the wittiest thing he could think of.

'Wanna lick of my lolly?'

She blushed slightly and looked at the other girl who was also very good-looking; her short black hair in a very well cut 'page-boy' style. She had lovely brown eyes which showed up against the almost white complexion of her face. David took the three pound bag of sugar from her and said, 'How come you're shifting these bags about — haven't you got a delivery man who brings?'

'Well we have,' she answered, 'but he hasn't come today, so we have to carry it.'

'Oh, I see,' said David. 'Well, I suppose we should intoduce ourselves.' He pointed to Geoff. 'He's Geoff and I'm Dave. Now what's your names?' he asked.

It was the first girl that answered him. 'Well,' she said, 'I'm Valerie and she's Wendy.'

David nodded and walked up a few stairs. 'Well, Valerie and Wendy,' he said, 'let's take this little lot up the stairs, shall we?'

The girls walked up behind him. They reached the cookery room.

'What time does your class start?' asked Wendy.

'How do you know that I'm in the tutorial?' asked David. 'I could be the plumber come to mend the drains.'

'Well I don't see your plunger,' she said.

'I don't use a plunger, I use my hands.' They all laughed. 'Anyway,' said David, 'the class starts at ten o'clook, normally, but today the teacher's a bit late for some reason. What do you do after cooking?' he asked, changing the subject.

'Well,' said Valerie, 'we finish cooking at half-past twelve and then we can go back to school for dinner, go home, or we can take some sandwiches and eat them in the park.'

'Which do you do?' asked Geoff.

'We bring some sandwiches and eat them in the park.'

'That's exactly what we do!' said David quickly. 'How about,' he went on, 'if him and me met you two in the park?'

The girls looked at each other and smiled. 'Alright,' said Valerie.

After they had taken the flour and sugar into the class for the girls, David and Geoff went downstairs where everybody was now entering the class. Mrs Cox had just come in and was opening the windows.

'How come you're so late?' asked Geoff on his way to the kettle.

'I couldn't get the car to start,' said Mrs Cox as she opened the window nearest the door. 'Anybody want any orange juice or lemonade?' she continued to David's thirsty relief.

Later on in the morning David and Geoff were sitting in the rest room eating the jam tarts that David did not manage to burn when Geoff asked: 'What do you think of it here?'

'To tell you the truth,' David said, 'if it wasn't for those two girls, I think I'd have bunked off this morning.'

'It is hard, I know,' said Geoff, 'but you'll get used to it.'

David nodded. He got up and walked to the window and looked out of it. A small brown dog on the other side of the road saw him and started barking. 'I wonder if I will,' he thought to himself. 'I wonder if I'll ever be able to face going anywhere like school again.' The brown dog stopped barking and ran down the road after a cat. 'Oh well,' thought David, 'only time will tell.' His thoughts were interrupted by the noise of the front door slamming and Mrs Cox coming into the room saying, 'Go downstairs with the others and have a game of football.' David and Geoff looked at each other. It was not that they did not like football. In fact, Geoff liked it very much. (David was not quite so keen. But there were much better things to do on a Thursday morning at a quarter to twelve, like sitting in the rest room eating jam tarts, for instance.)

'Do we have a choice?' asked Geoff.

'Yes,' replied Mrs Cox, 'football or English work books.'

'Where's the ball?' asked Geoff.

'It's downstairs. Simon, John and Christine are playing with it.'

David and Geoff went downstairs just in time to catch Simon and John teasing Christine. They would not let her play with the ball. After retrieving the ball from the boys, Geoff arranged a little match. Simon, John and Christine versus himself and David. When everybody was in position or, in this case, the nearest thing to it, Geoff kicked the ball into the middle of the playground. The match had started. Simon pounced on the ball straight away and kicked it against the wall. It rebounded to Christine who hurriedly tried to get rid of the 'horrid thing', as she called it. She took a swing at it but missed completely. David rushed at the ball, kicked it and sent it whizzing into John's (the goal-keeper) arms who, in turn, kicked back to David. Christine, seeing a chance for her to make up for her last mistake, and to wipe away the memory of having two 'I'm disgusted with you' expressions burning into her from Simon and John, focused her eyes on the ball and, with all the might she could summon, kicked it as hard as she could. She was surprised to hear a scream.

'Watch what you're doing!' yelled David. He was leaning against the wall, his face contorted with pain and nursing his injured shin.

'I'm sorry,' said Christine.

At half-past-twelve, after nursing his shin in the main room, David followed Geoff into the playground and out towards the park where they had arranged to meet the girls. The park was about a quarter of a mile away from the tutorial class and so they had all agreed this was a very convenient rendezvous.

The girls were sitting on the bench nearest the gate as Geoff and David crossed over the road towards them.

'Hello,' they said as the two boys sat down either side of them. David was the one that said 'hello' back as Geoff was too terrified to say anything.

This was the moment they had feared all morning. It had been easy talking to the girls on the stairs where it was dark and blushes were hard to see, but sitting next to them in a park in bright sunlight, well, that was a different matter. Would they be able to think of anything to say? Or would they just sit twiddling their thumbs? David noticed a bag of cakes laying on the bench next to Wendy. He seized a chance to break into conversation.

'What have you baked today?' he asked, relieving Geoff of trying to utter the first word that came into his head.

'They're fairy cakes,' she replied.

'Oh yes,' said Geoff, 'can I have one?'

'One what?' asked Wendy, turning to the other girl.

'One of your fairy cakes, of course! What did you think I mean?'

Wendy blushed and looked at Valerie. Geoff just smiled and accepted a cake. She offered David one.

'They're not bad,' mumbled David with a mouth full of cake. 'Do you like cooking?' he asked.

Valerie looked round at him. 'It's not bad,' she said, 'but I get a bit fed up with it because we have to do it whether we like to or not.'

David got up. 'Well,' he said, 'let's go for a walk.'

They strolled about for half an hour with David and Geoff talking about the tutorial class and the girls about their school until Wendy glanced at her watch.

'Oh dear,' she said, 'it's nearly half-past-one. She looked at Valerie. 'We'd better be getting back. Come on.'

After saying good-bye and arranging to meet the girls the same time the following week, David and Geoff went back to David's house where they spent the afternoon playing 'Monopoly'.

CHAPTER 5

SHOP WORK

David and Geoff saw the girls again the following week. This time they spent the lunch hour walking around the Tower of London, as the tutorial class was about a mile away from it.

Nothing interesting had happened at the class, or Penright's for that matter, until the Monday after. David and Geoff were in the painting room discussing the possibilities of West Ham beating Arsenal when Mrs Cox came into the room. She pulled a chair over to the table and told Geoff to do the same. David sat perched on the radiator with his feet resting on the work bench. Mrs Cox looked at Geoff.

'How would you like to go to school?' she asked.

'Why?'

'Well,' said Mrs Cox, 'you've been here over three months and you've shown great improvement, so we got in touch with the headmaster of a school I know.'

'What school's that?' asked Geoff anxiously.

'Selton.'

'Selton!' exclaimed Geoff. 'Not that one around the back of Cartridge Street?'

'That's the one. It's a school mainly for maladjusted children; which doesn't mean that you're maladjusted, but seeing as next year you'll be old enough to go out to work, Selton will toughen you up a bit, because this class is so peaceful that if you go out to work straight from here, it will be a very big jump, so therefore I think it will be best for you to go there.'

Geoff thought. He did not want to leave the tutorial class and Mrs Cox and David.

'When do I have to go?' he asked half-heartedly.

'The beginning of next term. It's July now, so you've got the next month and a half to prepare for it. Two weeks here and a month or so for the school holidays,' Mrs Cox replied. Geoff thought for a moment.

'I suppose I'll have to go then,' he said.

'I'll phone Mr Reed, he's the headmaster, and you should get a letter in a few days telling you when to go up to the school for an interview.' She turned to David. 'And who knows,' she said, 'you might go there as well.' David laughed.

'No, not me,' he said, 'I'm not *that* unlucky!' He thought maybe he *was* that unlucky! He knew deep down inside that he, not unlike Geoff, did not want to leave the comfortable shell of the class.

At twelve-thirty when the class finished, Geoff said goodbye to David and made his way to Penright's Supermarket, thinking all the time of Selton. He reached the doors of the shop just in time to see the manager, Mr Pitfield, bending over a sixty-pound box of cheese. With a superhuman effort Mr Pitfield managed to stagger over to the conveyor belt; he dropped the cheese on to it with a thud. He looked around, his face was a bright red and he was puffing and blowing. Gradually, his normal colour came back. He saw Geoff come through the doors.

'Give us a hand with this lot,' he shouted over to Geoff. He definitely needed help.

There were boxes of tomato soup, cornflakes, cheeses, drinks and, leaning up against the wall were stacks of biscuits. There were also boxes of fruit scattered here and there.

Every Monday morning was the shop's delivery day which was the reason why the stock was lying around.

'You go downstairs,' said Mr Pitfield to Geoff as he picked up two boxes with great effort, 'and I'll shove this lot down the conveyor belt to yer.'

'Alright,' said Geoff.

Geoff went through the door that led down to the warehouse below the shop and descended the stairs. He walked over to the conveyor belt and looked up where he could see the head and shoulders of the manager peering down at him from the top of the belt. He shouted up to Mr Pitfield.

'Okay, you can send the stuff down.'

Mr Pitfield pressed a button at the side of the conveyor belt which sent boxes and packages sliding down to Geoff who had to heave the load off the belt and place it down on the floor, then rush back to the conveyor belt in time to catch the next item. And so it went on, until the conveyor was silent except for the banging of the last few boxes that came down it.

'Only some cheeses to come down now,' Mr Pitfield shouted down the conveyor belt to Geoff. He placed a Dutch Gouda on to the belt, then two more. Then he almost threw one on; it crashed down the conveyor belt, bouncing against one wall, then the other towards the terrified Geoff who just stood with his mouth open watching twelve pounds of Dutch Gouda cheese flying towards him. He glanced up to see the flustered figure of the manager watching in utter horror as the cheese thudded to a halt into Geoff's stomach.

'For God's sake' shouted the manager, 'don't drop the cheese!'

'Balls to the cheese,' thought Geoff rubbing his stomach. He dropped the cheese down on one of the racks.

'How's yer gut?' asked Mr Pitfield, as he piled up the last of the cheese.

Geoff didn't answer; he just kept rubbing his painful injury.

'Usually,' went on Mr Pitfield, 'the cheese would have been in a box, but that burke of a delivery man split it when he wheeled it in.'

By the time everything was down in the warehouse, the floor around the conveyor was in a terrible mess and it took Geoff most of the day to tidy everything up. He had no-one to help him because Bert (the man who normally helped Geoff) was up in the shop helping the manager. The man that normally helped the manager was away on holiday. There were just a few empty boxes to stack away, so after putting two boxes of eggs on the shelves, he sent the empty boxes up the conveyor belt so they could be used in the shop. He had just put the last box on the conveyor belt when he had an uncontrollable urge to stuff a box of margarine in it.

'Sod Penright,' he thought, 'I've been rupturing myself for weeks shifting bleeding boxes about and I don't get any thanks or good money so I deserve something.'

He looked round. There was no-one about so he quickly put the box of margarine into the empty egg box and covered it with rubbish. He then sent the two empty egg boxes up the conveyor belt. He stopped the belt when they reached the top; he ran up the stairs through the door and over to the conveyor belt where he lifted the boxes off and then took them outside and put them onto the pavement for the dustmen to collect. His idea was to come out of the shop and, when everybody had left, he would sort through the pile of empty boxes, take out the margarine and go home. It all went as planned.

Mr Pitfield locked up the shop as usual at five-thirty and Geoff made it look as if he was going home. He crossed over the road and waited round the corner until everyone had gone. He found the egg boxes and inside were the thiry-six cartons of margarine.

'Thank God,' Geoff said to himself, 'nobody's touched them.' He picked the margarine up and walked down the road. He crossed over and walked along St. Christopher Road toward Roverhill House where he lived. He had gone halfway up the road when all of a sudden he heard a high-pitched screech of car tyres. He looked round. A blue police panda car had pulled up beside him.

'Oh shit!' thought Geoff. 'How did they find out? Now I'm for it!'

A policeman looked out of the window.

'Come 'ere son,' he said in a deep voice. Geoff swallowed. What could he say? He walked slowly over to the policeman, all the time trying to conceal the margarine. The policeman looked at him through hard grey eyes.

'Can you tell me where Potter Street is?' he asked.

Geoff gave a sigh of relief. 'Yeah,' he mumbled. 'It's the next turning on yer left.'

'Ta very much,' said the policeman. He wound the window up and the car sped down the road.

Geoff walked on until he reached the entrance of the car park of Roverhill House. He walked through the car park and past the sheds that the residents used to keep prams and such things in. Number One Roverhill House where Geoff lived was directly opposite the sheds. He went up to the door, took the key out of his pocket and opened it and went in. He walked into the kitchen where his mother was cooking the dinner.

'Look what I've got,' announced Geoff proudly. His mother looked round at the margarine in Geoff's arms.

'Where did you get that?' she asked.

'I got it from work,' answered Geoff.

'How did you get it from work?'

'Somebody gave it to me.'

'Who?'

'Mr. Pitfield,' said Geoff quickly.

'Now listen,' said Geoff's mother. 'Now I know that you stole it. Mr Pitfield's Scrooge number two. He wouldn't give anything away!'

Geoff stood looking down at his shoes.

'I don't like you stealing things. Understand?'

'Yes,' said Geoff slowly.

'Now promise me you won't do it again.'

'I won't,' said Geoff quietly. He walked out of the room and went over to his bicycle which was propped up against the wall in the passage. He lifted the top of the saddle bag open and put the margarine into it. He wheeled the bicycle over to the front door and opened it. He then pushed the bicycle   out of the door and stood ready to close it.

'I'm just going to David's,' shouted Geoff towards the kitchen.

'Well don't be long. We're going to have dinner soon,' came the reply.

Geoff decided that as there were so many cartons of margarine, he would give some to David's mother. He pushed the pedal down and rode off to David's house. Five minutes later he turned down into Little Turner Street, stopped outside number seventy-eight, got off the bicycle and gave three loud knocks on the door.

'Hello Geoff,' said a voice somewhere above him. Geoff looked up and saw David's head sticking out of the third floor window.

'For what do we honour this visit, pray tell?' asked David.

'I've got a little present for you,' grinned Geoff.

'Oh yes,' said the interested David. 'What is it?'

'It's some boxes. Look, stop playing silly buggers and throw down the key will yer.'

'Oh sorry,' said David, who wasn't really sorry at all. David threw his door key down and Geoff opened the door and put his bike — 'Crankshaft' as he liked to call it because it was so old — in the passage. He took the margarine out of the saddlebag and walked up the stairs and in to the kitchen where Mrs Cook was also preparing dinner. David came in and retrieved his key.

'Now,' said David, 'what's this little present then?'

'Oh that,' said Geoff. 'Well you see', he went on, 'the manager of the shop I work at gave me these boxes of margarine.' He showed the margarine to Mrs Cook and David. 'Yer see, I done him a favour last week and he gave me this for it. And he gave me such a lot that we couldn't fit it in our fridge, so I thought you might like some.'

'That's very nice of you Geoff' said Mrs Cook. She turned to David. 'Now we can have margarine for breakfast for the next ten years,' she laughed. She took the fifteen cartons of margarine from Geoff and put them in the fridge.

'Well,' said Geoff, 'I must be going because my Mum's made my dinner.'

'I'll see you down to the door,' said David. They walked down the stairs and into the passage. David looked at Geoff and whispered, 'Where did you really get that margarine from?'

'I told you, from my manager.'

'Look,' said David, 'I know you, you're the Artful Dodger of the East End. Now where did you get it?'

Geoff grinned. 'It fell off the back of a conveyor belt.'

'What?' said David, rather perplexed.

'It fell off the back of a conveyor belt,' repeated Geoff.

CHAPTER 6

JUDO JIM

'Look,' said David, 'stop messing around and tell me where you got the margarine from.'

'I nicked it, you idiot!' shouted Geoff.

'Oh,' said David slowly, 'I was right, you did nick it!'

Geoff sighed. 'I've had enough of you,' he said, 'you're driving me up the wall. Every time I say anything, you repeat it. For God's sake, shut up!'

'Oh, sorry,' said David.

'Anyway,' said Geoff, opening the door. 'I've got to get going now 'cos me mum's making me dinner.' He put the bicycle in the road and got on. I think I might come round and pay you a visit later on,' he said.

'Well you can't, not tonight,' said David.

'Why not?'

'Because I'm going to Judo,' answered David.

Geoff looked surprised. He couldn't imagine David doing Judo. He always thought it was only secret agents like James Bond that did Judo. He laughed.

'Dont' tell me that *you* do Judo', he said.

'Well I do,' replied David.

'How long have you been doing it?' enquired Geoff.

'About two-and-a-half years.'

'Where do you do it then?'

'Over at the girls' school. At night. It's a youth club. They have all sorts of things; like judo, table tennis, football, badminton and loads of other things. Why don't you come over there?'

'No, not me,' answered Geoff. 'I don't fancy being thrown around by some dirty great bloke. I like to know that I can win. And, anyway, I'd look bleedin' silly in a Judo suit.'

'Yeah, you would!' laughed David. 'No, seriously, you should come over there. You never know, you might be able to throw everybody around. And you see, if you come over there, I can get my own back and throw you around.' He laughed.

'No,' said Geoff, shaking his head. 'I might get hurt.'

'Of course you won't,' said David. 'You don't get thrown around, well, not until you can breakfall properly. Anyway, come on! Why not give it a try? There's a great crowd over at the club.' He started counting on his fingers. 'There's my brother Stephen, there's Mr Jones the instructor, he's a fifth

Dan.'

'A what?' interrupted Geoff.

'A fifth Dan.'

'What's that?'

'Well,' said David, 'a black belt isn't the highest belt you know. Once you get to your black belt, there's grades above it, and that's what a dan is. It means 'step'. So the first black belt is called the first Dan and the next is second. And so on and so on.'

'What's the highest then?' asked Geoff.

'I suppose it's about 10th Dan, but by the time you get to 10th Dan you're about ninety odd so nobody really gets any higher.'

'Is your instructor a high grade?' enquired Geoff.

'Yeah, he is,' answered David.

'Well,' smiled Geoff. 'That's another reason for not going.' He pushed down on the pedal. 'I'll see you tomorrow, Judo Jim,' he said.

David watched Geoff go up to the top of the street and turn into the main road. He went in and shut the door behind him. He walked up the stairs and into the kitchen.

'Come on,' said Mrs Cook. 'Hurry up and wash your hands, we're having dinner now.'

David washed his hands and sat down at the table next to his brother Stephen. About half-way through the meal David turned to his mother. 'Geoff's going to another school,' he said.

'Oh yes,' said Mrs Cook. 'Which one?'

'Selton.'

Stephen suddenly started coughing and spluttering as if he had swallowed too much food at once. 'Not that nut-house down near Cartridge Street?' he asked in surprised tones.

'Yes, that one,' answered David.

'He's mad, going there,' said Stephen.

Paul, who was sitting at the other end of the table interrupted. 'Isn't it a special school?' he asked.

'Yes' answered David. 'It's a school for maladjusted kids.'

'Is Geoff maladjusted then?'

'No, but Mrs Cox said, that seeing as Geoff's leaving school next year, Selton will toughen him up a bit before he goes to work.'

'Toughen him up!' said Stephen, 'It'll kill him!'

They all started laughing.

Mrs. Cook spoke. 'When is he going?' she asked.

'At the beginning of September. After the summer holidays.'

'Does he want to go?'

'I'm not sure,' said David.

After dinner David and Stephen went and packed their things for Judo. David went down to his bedroom and took his judo suit out of his cupboard. He folded the jacket and trousers and put them neatly in his holdall. Then he rolled his towel up and put it on top of the rest of the suit. (His towel was for the shower afterwards.) He then put his belt on top of the towel with his judo slippers. David picked up his holdall and went downstairs where Stephen was waiting for him. David was proud of his judo holdall, it looked very impressive. When he had first got it, it was just a normal black holdall; so David decided to smarten it up a bit. His eldest brother Paul had got his A-level Art and he said that he would help. It took Paul three days to paint the words 'British Judo Association' on the side of it in white paint, but it was worth it. It did look very impressive. David had decided to try his hand at painting the holdall. So, on the other side, he put what he thought (he copied the Japanese from a poster on Judo he had) was Japanese for 'Judo'. But Stephen said that it probably read, 'Joe's Cafe' or something like it.

David shut the door and the two boys walked up the street. The girl's school where David did judo was just around the corner from Little Turner Street, so it only took them a few minutes to go through the gates and walk towards the changing room along a narrow concrete path. David thought it strange that he could go to judo, as it was a modern comprehensive school, not unlike the first secondary school he had been to, where all his troubles had started. Most schools he found impossible to go into whatever the reason, even if it was for judo, which was always at night, so the routine was not at all like school.

He was still wondering when a deep cockney voice came from from behind him. 'Give us yer money or I'll jump yer,' it said. David and Stephen turned round and saw a boy, about thirteen years old with long fair hair who was about the same height as David, and he had a wide smile on his face. 'Now tell the truth,' the boy said. His voice was about two octaves higher now. 'I frightened the life out of you, didn't I?'

'Oh yeah,' said David, 'of course you did. I was just wondering how Stephen was going to handle you if you were a big geezer.'

The boy laughed. 'Where were you going then?' he asked.

'Me? I was going to get help,' came the reply.

'Coward' laughed the boy.

'Michael,' said David, 'you are definitely touched.'

'Right,' said Michael, 'just you wait until I get you on that mat.

I'm going to kill you!'

'Kill me?' laughed David, 'you couldn't kill a wet paper bag.'

Stephen interrupted. 'Come on you two,' he said, 'stop peeing around and go and get changed.'

'Alright,' said David.

David and Michael followed Stephen up the stairs next to the two gymnasiums and into the changing rooms. David threw his holdall onto the bench that ran all the way round the room. As far as David knew all judo players seemed to do this. They always dropped them on the floor or threw them on a chair. The reason was unknown to David. He looked round the room. There were only four other people in the room apart from Michael, Stephen and himself. Bill, yellow belt, Alan, a green belt, Philip a brown belt and George, David Cook's life-long friend/enemy. Bill Green was the first to look up as David, Michael and Stephen came in.

'It's the three stooges,' he laughed.

The others looked up. Philip Banks, who was the second highest grade of the class called, 'Where have you lot been? It's ten past. You're ten minutes late.' He tried to sound important. Stephen laughed.

'Listen Togo,' he said, 'if you don't behave yourself, I'll have to knock you around a bit when we get downstairs.'

Philip grinned. 'I'll take you up on that,' he said. He put his shoes under the bench, picked up his bag and walked over to the door. He turned to Stephen. 'And don't make too much noise!'

Stephen picked up his towel and threw it at Philip who shielded himself with the door. He picked up the towel, threw it back at Stephen and ran down the stairs, laughing.

'Silly idiot!' said Stephen.

He quickly changed, put on his blue belt and went downstairs after telling David, Michael and George to hurry up. Alan, the green belt, went down with him. The three remaining boys got changed in silence until David asked George, 'George, did you have a bath last night?'

'No,' answered George Croft.

'Oh, that's funny, I could have sworn it was smelling a bit sweeter in here.' He laughed.

George just mumbled something and continued to get changed. George was not very well liked in the class. In fact a few people couldn't stand to be in the same room as him. There were probably two reasons for this. The first being that George was very unlikeable and would do very strange things. For instance, he invited David, Michael and a few of their friends around to his house to a party after saying that there would be 'tons of girls' there. When David and Michael reached his house, George would not let them in. He said he couldn't get anybody to come and that his mother and father were having visitors so he could not let David, Michael and their friends in. For a fabulous party it was very uneventful!.

George had also a very annoying habit of disappearing whenever he was walking along with David or somebody. One minute he would be talking quite normally and the next he would be running up the road and leaving whoever he was with. The natural conclusion for David to reach was that George didn't want him around. But this was not so. David had known George all his life. And he had always been very strange. Every time David thought that he had seen the last of George, he would turn up weeks later out of the blue with some story about spending the previous week in the Costa del Sol, knowing full well that David had seen him get on a bus two days before!

The second reason for people not wanting to stay in the same room as George was probably because he had terrible body odour. He didn't bath for months on end. He was known by his enemies by the affectionate name of 'the green mist'. George never failed to amaze everybody.

The three boys went downstairs and into the gymnasium. It was a very small class. On a good day there would be only ten people, but David didn't mind; he always said that a crowded mat can be dangerous with everybody pushing around and rolling about on it. David and everybody else did some 'loosening up' exercises to warm up. After that, David and Michael went to a corner of the mat and practised the Nage-no-kata, a set of fifteen throws. After about three-quarters-of-an-hour practising certain throws and holds it was time for everybody to have a 'Randorie', a free practice where the judo players have a chance to practice all their throws and holds they know. The Randories lasted until eight-forty-five when Mr Jones told everybody to line up in front of him and bow. This was performed at the end of every lesson; it is to show courtesy to the instructor and to thank him and the rest of the class for practising. Judo should be very polite.

David got changed and went home determined to throw Stephen and to get Geoff to go to judo. Yes, he had definitely made up his mind the next time he came he would have Geoff with him.

CHAPTER 7

THE LAST WEEK

'Well this is it', Geoff thought as he walked up the stairs towards the tutorial class. 'One more week here. I'll be sorry to go. He reminisced on the 'good times' he and David had had. Geoff opened the familiar door of the class and walked in and closed the door behind him.

'Good morning', said Mrs Cox cheerfully. She looked at Geoff's worried face. 'Cheer up', she said, 'it may never happen'.

'But it already has', said Geoff sadly.

'Look', said Mrs Cox, 'I know it's hard for you to make a sudden change from here to another school, especially if you've been coming to a class like this for a few months'. She paused, 'So I have made a little arrangement with Selton'.

'What kind of arrangement?' asked the anxious Geoff.

'Well' continued Mrs Cox, 'for three days a week you'll attend Selton and for the other two days you will come here. So the change will be gradual'.

Geoff's face brightened up. 'How long will I come here for two days a week?' he asked.

'For about a month', answered Mrs Cox. 'Then a month at one morning, and then after that you'll be a Seltonite full time,' she smiled.

'I'll go and put the kettle on', said Geoff, pleased by the arrangement. He went in to the other room. The door opened and Geoff popped his head out into the passage to see who it was. 'It's Judo Jim', he announced sarcastically as David walked through the doorway.

'If you don't shut up shorty', smiled David, 'I'll throw you by your balls'.

A voice came from the main room where Mrs Cox was sitting writing something. 'What was that?' she asked.

'His balls, Miss. Balls of his feet', answered David.

David helped Geoff take in the coffee. Geoff put the tray with three cups on it on Mrs Cox's desk. The two boys took their cups off the tray and balanced them on their laps after they sat down.

'What did you used to do before you got offered this job?' asked Geoff.

'I used to teach at a girls' school', answered Mrs Cox, 'it was a Special School. All the girls were pregnant'. David and Geoff listened in fascination. Mrs Cox continued. 'They were girls from eleven to eighteen. Every one pregnant'.

'That's a weird kind of job', interrupted David.

'Well', remarked Mrs Cox, 'I'm a weird kind of person'.

Geoff changed the subject. 'How many classes like this are there?' he asked.

'There are quite a few. Something like fifty in London. They're mostly scattered around the poorer areas. Like Stepney and places like it.

'Why's that?'

'Because most of the problem children come from the poorer areas of London. Not all of them. But quite a few'.

'Why does this class help children with problems?' asked Geoff.

'Well', answered Mrs Cox, 'most problem children just can't take the pressure of a normal school. Whatever their problem is. You see, in a normal school, they're being pressurised all the time. 'Do this. Do that', and if children have problems at home, then they just can't cope with anything in school. They start playing truant and they disrupt the class. And so coming here helps them cope with their problems.'

'How?'

'Well normally the child is under a psychiatrist when he's sent here and so when he's here he's not pressurised and also he's seeing the psychiatrist and having treatment and that helps him overcome his problem. Take little John for instance, or Simon; they're just a little backward. So they come here three mornings a week and they go to their normal schools for the rest of the week'.

'Do the women that bring them get paid, or do they just volunteer?' enquired Geoff.

'You're asking a lot of questions aren't you?' said Mrs Cox looking at the two boys.

'Well', said David, 'we're nosey'.

Mrs Cox laughed. 'Oh well, if you're that nosey, I suppose I'd better answer your questions. The women do get paid. Not a lot but they do get paid'. The door opened and Simon came running in followed by Mrs Price, one of the women that worked as an escort for the smaller children.

'Hello', said Simon as he went to his work drawer and took out a packet of wine gums. Mrs Cox smiled at Mrs Price and picked up the coffee percolator. 'Do you want some coffee?', she asked.

'No thanks', came the reply. Geoff started laughing.

'What's so funny?', enquired Mrs Cox.

Geoff forced himself to stop. 'You know the one thing I'll

55

always remember you for is when anybody comes up here, the first thing you say is, 'Do you want some coffee'.'

'And you're forever putting the kettle on', smiled Mrs Cox.

'I really must go', said Mrs Price, 'We've got lots of washing and tidying up to do. It's always the same on Mondays. I'll be back at half past twelve. Bye'. She walked out and closed the door.

David turned to Simon. 'How many wine gums have you got in that draw?' he asked.

'Only twelve', answered Simon. 'Do you want one?' He reached over to the drawer and took out another packet and offered it around. Mrs Cox was very strict on this. If anybody came in with a packet of sweets, she insisted that they hand them round.

The door opened and John came running in. He stopped abruptly with his feet together and his hands by his side. 'Hello' he said loudly.

The door opened again and in walked Mrs Green, John's escort. 'I don't know how he does it', she gasped, 'God knows where he gets his energy from. I really don't know'.

It was eleven-thirty and David and Geoff were busy working in their English books when Simon came running into the room. 'Those two girls that you met from the cookery class are outside', he announced in a loud voice.

'Ha ha', said David, 'very funny. But you don't think we're going to fall for that trick do you?'

'But they are', Simon repeated.

'Pull the other one, it's got bells on', said Geoff sarcastically.

'Don't you believe me?' asked Simon.

'No we don't', answered David. 'Look, they do cooking on Thursday and today's Monday'.

'But we just seen 'em', Simon said in desperate tones. David looked at Geoff and shrugged his shoulders.

'Let's have a look', he said. They got up and walked over to the door and opened it.

David popped his head out to the stairs. 'Well, where are they?' he asked.

'They must be upstairs'.

'I think you're joking', said Geoff. They heard voices coming from up the stairs. Then the shapely figures of Valerie and Wendy came into sight.

'I told you', grinned Simon.

Geoff bent down to him. 'If you don't go inside, I'll stick your head down the loo', he said quietly.

'Alright, I'm going', said Simon. He went in and closed the

door.

'I thought you had cooking on Thursday?' Geoff asked as the girls came down to the landing.

'We do', answered Wendy, 'but the teacher that normally takes us for cooking is ill, so one of the other teachers is taking us in her free period'.

'We'll see you after class then', said David. The girls nodded. 'Bye', they said.

Walking around Stepney can be fun when you have got beside you two of the best-looking girls in London.

'Do you live near here?' Geoff asked Valerie.

'Yes, I live in Truman Close', she said pointing to a high tower block at the bottom of the road. 'Come in', she said, 'let's go upstairs for a cup of tea'.

'You're beginning to sound like Mrs Cox', laughed Geoff.

They followed Wendy and Valerie in to the flats and waited for the lift. The lift came, they walked in and Valerie pressed the button for the ninth floor. A few seconds later the lift door opened and everyone came out. It was a fairly modern block of flats, perhaps two or three years old. The ninth floor had a long corridor with about eight doors all the same, dark blue. They walked halfway down the corridor until Valerie stopped outside number forty-seven. Valerie took out the door key and they walked into the hallway.

It was a pleasant-looking flat. On the floor was a lush red carpet; decorating the walls was a light blue wallpaper. The four of them walked through the hallway. Valerie opened the door of the living room and gestured that David and Geoff should go in. Wendy went into the kitchen to make some coffee. 'It's all right', she said, 'my Mum and Dad's at work, so you can make as much noise as you like. Sit down if you like'.

David sat next to Geoff on the black settee and Valerie sat in the corner in a big black armchair. David looked round the room. Above the gas fire the wall was covered with artificial bricks that were supposed to look real. On the two alcoves beside it was bright orange wallpaper which blended well with the orange carpet and orange drapes. The other walls all had the same white wallpaper that stood out against the black three-piece suite. On the wall opposite the window was a huge picture of the Italian Riviera. The room had every colour of the rainbow in it, but none of the colours clashed. In the corner stood a television; next to it was a matching stereogram that stretched half the length of the wall.

Valerie walked over to the stereogram and pulled out the record rack that was underneath it. She started to sift through it, occasionally stopping to take a record out and put it on the floor beside her. She picked up the records and piled them, one on top of each other on the spindle and placed the overarm on top of them. She pushed the operating control up to 'auto' and put the lid of the stereogram down again; there was a sharp 'click' and the first record began to play. Geoff rose from the settee, walked over to the record rack and started to look through it. A few seconds later he said, 'let's put this one on, it's slower'. He winked at Valerie who blushed slightly. He took the pile of records off and put the record he had chosen on. Wendy came through the door carrying a tray of coffee. She put the tray down on the small coffee table in the middle of the room. David came to take a cup from the tray.

'Do you wanna dance?' Geoff asked Valerie as he stood up.

'Yes. Alright', smiled Valerie. She put her cup down and put her arms round Geoff and they began to sway gently to the soft music. David plucked up courage and asked Wendy to dance. And then there were two couples gently swaying in the middle of the room. Geoff pulled Valerie closer towards him and kissed her soft cheek. Very soon the whole room seemed to fill with passion. Geoff moved forward ready to kiss Valerie's soft lips. She moved back, and seemed to make up her mind. Their lips came closer and closer together. They both closed their eyes and waited for that deep passionate moment. It did not come. Suddenly the door swung open. Geoff opened his eyes and, standing in the doorway he saw the biggest man he had ever seen. The man took up the whole doorway with his huge frame. He was no shorter than six feet seven and he must have weighed at least twenty stone. Geoff swallowed.

'What the hell's going on?' the man asked, never once taking his eyes off of Geoff or David.

'We're having a cup of coffee Dad', answered Valerie in a trembling voice.

'Do you always drink coffee while you dance?' enquired Valerie's father in disbelieving tones.

'Only when we're thirsty', answered Geoff who resented the idea of being pushed around. He thought of what he had just said. 'Oh no, why did I say that? He'll kill me!' Geoff and David waited for the man to charge towards them in a fierce temper. But no. For the second time that afternoon the unexpected happened. The huge man was laughing.

'That's good', he chuckled. 'Very funny. I couldn't have done better myself'. The man walked over to the settee and lay down on it. The boys suddenly realised why the huge Goliath was laughing. He was drunk. The man insisted that the boys stay and tell him a few jokes and talk. The reason he was home so early he told them was because a friend that he worked with was getting married the next day, so they had all had a drink and he had decided to come home. 'A drink', thought David, 'he must have had bucketfulls of the stuff!'

After an hour of David and Geoff listening to the man's terrible jokes and singing, Valerie finally persuaded her father to let the boys go as they all had to get back to school. The only reason he agreed was the fact he was slowly falling asleep. Before the boys said 'goodbye' to Valerie and Wendy, Geoff asked, 'Is he always like that?'

'Yes. All the time', answered Valerie.

The boys turned round and walked into the lift. 'Jesus Christ', said David, 'I never want to go up there again!'

'Yeah', agreed Geoff, 'I think we had better forget about those girls. They're too dangerous'.

When Geoff arrived at Penright's supermarket again, not unlike other Mondays, there were various boxes everywhere. Mr Pitfield called Geoff over. 'Now look Geoff', he said, 'I'm going downstairs and will take the stuff off the conveyor belt that you send down. Alright?'

'Alright', said Geoff.

The manager walked over to the door of the warehouse. 'And you count up how many items there are', he said. But Geoff did not hear. He still had his mind on the events that had happened that afternoon. Mr Pitfield's voice came up from the warehouse. 'Okay', he shouted. 'Send the stuff down'.

Geoff put three boxes, one after the other on the conveyor belt. Then some big boxes of sugar and flour. He sent down huge boxes of biscuits, cheese, and dozens of other things.

'How many?' wheezed Mr Pitfield as he came through the doorway.

'How many what?' asked Geoff.

'How many articles were there?' shouted the manager as he picked up one of the order forms that were by the side of the conveyor belt.

'I don't know', answered Geoff. 'I didn't count them'.

The manager had an expression that suggested that he was going to hit Geoff's head with the nearest thing he could get hold of, or burst out crying. 'What the bloody hell did I say to you before I went downstairs?' he shouted.

'Send this lot down, or something like that' answered Geoff.

'And then what did I say?' asked the impatient manager.

'I didn't hear the next thing you said'.

'I said count the lot', bellowed Mr Pitfield. 'Now everything is packed away, I don't know what the new stock is or the old stock'. He wiped the sweat away from his forehead with his arm and banged his hands down onto the conveyor belt. 'Never mind', he said, 'but make sure you hear me next time or you'll be out on your arse'.

Geoff felt a touch of nostalgia as he finished his last full week at the tutorial class. It was 12.30 on the Friday and everybody was preparing to go home.

'Now remember', said Mrs Cox to all the children. 'Look after yourselves and don't get into any trouble during the holidays and I'll see you all in six weeks time, and Geoff I'll see you every Tuesday and Wednesday'. She waited until everybody had gone and then she locked the door.

Geoff left David at the top of Little Turner Street and walked home. He was looking forward to the six week holiday, because then he could get about more than he had done when he was too terrified to step out of his house. He thought of Selton and wondered if all his troubles would start again.

'We'll see', he thought. 'We'll see'.

CHAPTER 8

NO RIDING PLACE

Among the many places that David and Geoff rode to on their bicycles during the summer holidays, the one place and time they would always remember was the time they decided to visit George. Not because they liked his company but because George knew a lot of girls. Which was not very surprising as George's next door neighbours were three sisters, all the same age as himself. Being triplets, George could never tell one from the other but he did not mind. In fact, he thought it was quite 'a laugh'.

It was 7.30 on Friday, 19th August. A few weeks before the schools would be going back and Geoff would be starting Selton. Geoff and David had come to the conclusion that if they were to meet some girls they would have to put themselves out. George lived four miles away from David so it took him and Geoff about half an hour to get there on their bikes. Geoff had already met George as George had once come up to the tutorial with a message for David. They turned down Formby Street and rode down towards Bank House, a small block of flats where George lived. Geoff and David got into the lift with their bicycles and pressed for the fourth floor.

They reached the floor and wheeled the machines over to the wall outside number twenty-eight and locked them up. David rang on the door bell. A few seconds later, George's mop of hair on top of an acne-riddled face appeared round the door. 'Hello, what do you want?' asked the face.

'We've come to visit you and to comfort you in your hour of need,' answered David sarcastically. 'Well, aren't you going to let us in? We'll melt if we're left out in the air too long.'

'Er well,' said George slowly, 'I can't let you in now because Sharon, Rose and June (the neighbours) are in me room and me mum are in the front room watching telly and they don't want any of me mates in the house because they're watching their favourite programme and they don't want a lot of noise.'

'What?' asked the confused Geoff.

'Me mum and Dad are watching the box and they don't want to be disturbed by any of me mates, you two.'

'I'm even more confused now,' said Geoff.

'Come on George,' pleaded David, 'Let us in.'

'I can't'.

'Why not,'

'I told yer. Me mum and Dad.'

'Look,' said David. 'You've got three birds in your room. And there's three of us. Come on, let us in.'

'I can't,' were George's last words before he slammed the door in his 'friends'' faces. The two stunned boys stood for a few seconds looking at the closed door in amazement.

'Bastard,' was the only word David could mutter. David and Geoff went to the lift and waited until the door opened. They got in and descended to the ground floor. They rode down to the main road.

'If he wasn't so bloody big I'd do him in' remarked Geoff.

'That wouldn't do any good. Then we'd never have a chance with the girls.'

'Yeah, I suppose you're right,' said Geoff, 'but what are we going to do. We'll have to get our own back. We can't let him get away with that.'

David suddenly pulled into the kerb and braked sharply. He looked at Geoff and smiled.

'I think,' he said, 'I've got an idea.'

Geoff listened with interest.

'Well,' continued David, 'why did we go round to George's to-night.'

'To try and get off with the girls of course,' answered Geoff.

'Exactly,' said David. 'The girls are the only reason we came here, 'right''.

'Right.'

'Well then,' he went on, 'if we could chat up the girls and get them to come round our way. Apart from getting off with them, we'd also be getting our own back on the 'Green Mist', because we'd be going with his girls and he'd have to stay at home and twiddle his thumbs.'

'That's a good idea,' said Geoff, 'but how are we going to chat up the girls if they're always in his house and he won't let us in?'

David thought for a minute.

'If there's one thing that George likes,' he said, 'it's a bit of flattery, and the more the better. So if we go up to him tomorrow afternoon and we go out on the bikes with him and tell him how 'wonderfully marvellous' he is, then, by tomorrow night he'll think we're great and he'll ask us to go up to his house, and that's when we'll chat up the girls.'

'That's not a bad idea,' remarked Geoff.

'Not bad,' grinned David, 'it's terrific!'

It was 10 o'clock when David and Geoff knocked on the door of number 28 Bank House the next day, and it was 1.15 after a lot of 'I wish I was as clever as you George' talk from both

David and Geoff that the two managed to get George to come out on his bicycle with them. While George pumped up his front tyre outside Bank House, Geoff could not help smiling as he looked at George's bicycle. He thought that it looked just like 'Piccadilly Circus', only on wheels. On the front of the bicycle were two reflectors and a big lamp, and on the back, on either side of the rear wheel were two orange indicators which were controlled by two buttons on the handlebars. The word 'ZAP' stretched the length of the top bar of the bright green frame. The pump had long coloured tassles hanging on it which matched the ones that hung from both ends of the handlebars. On the spokes of both wheels were different bits of coloured sticky tape, so that when the machine was moving the wheels looked like two huge catherine wheels. In fact the whole 'rigmarole' could be described by one word. Sick. On the side of the bicycle was a small cannister that David had never seen.

'What's that —' he asked as George put the pump back onto the bicycle and got on.

'It's a horn' said George proudly, 'I'll show yer.' He pushed the button down that was on the top of the cannister. There was an ear piercing noise not unlike that of a fire engine siren and George rode down the street after frightening the life out of an old woman who was crossing the street at the time.

David and Geoff caught George up.

'Where we going?' asked David.

'Let's go over the cat-walk,' said George.

'Alright.' The 'cat-walk' was the local name for a long path that ran down a high hill in the park that was about 2 miles away from George's house.

'Yerst,' said George as the three boys rode along. 'I know the cat-walk well. You oughter to see the way I turn the corners.'

'Yeah,' said Geoff, 'I'd love to see yer.'

David and Geoff had gone over the cat-walk once or twice before and they knew how difficult it was to keep their balance riding along a two foot wide path. The path ran down the front of the hill. It had a lot of bushes either side of the path so you had to be very careful and make sure you did not come off the path. The three boys rode into the park. A few minutes later they reached the top of the hill and rode over to the beginning of the 'cat-walk'. They stood and looked down at the path that wound itself 150 feet down to the bottom of the park.

'Okay,' said George, 'all you've got to do is to follow me down and you'll be alright.'

They rode down to the first bend with George talking all the time telling them how good he was at that sort of thing and that a lot of people had come off the path at the bends and that he would never do that. They raced down to the second bend.

'Now lean over' were George's last words before David and Geoff saw him and his bicycle shoot off the bend and fall 10 feet into the bushes below. They could do nothing but laugh at the sight of the flustered, sore, figure of George looking up to them with his 'Piccadilly Circus' on wheels lying on top of him.

'Bloody Hell,' shouted George, his voice trembling with shock.

Because George had injured himself (cut his finger) and buckled both wheels of his beloved bicycle he did not invite David and Geoff around that night.

During the week following the accident, David and Geoff realised only too well that they had still not got friendly with Rose, Sharon and June. So on Thursday night they decided to go to Bank House, but not on their bicycles, and try and see the girls. So that night after Geoff finished work at Penrights they set off to the bus-stop.

Ten minutes later the bus came and they got on and went upstairs. It took 15 minutes for the bus to reach Formby Street. The boys got up and pressed the bell, the bus slowed down for just enough time for Geoff and David to jump off.

They waited for the lift to come and then went to the fourth floor. After a few minutes of ringing the girls' doorbell, David and Geoff realised that nobody was in.

'That was a wasted journey, wasn't it?' said David.

'Yes it was' remarked Geoff.

The two miserable boys went down again and walked towards the bus-stop. They waited for about half an hour until a bus that looked as if it was going to collapse came along. They got on and sat at the front of the bus.

A few seconds later the bus conductor came up. He was a small man and he gave the boys a strange look as he took their two three pence fares.

The conductor went downstairs again and the bus continued on its journey.

Five minutes later the conductor came up again.

'Okay you two,' he said in a loud voice.

'That'll be another two pence.'

The boys fished in their pockets and found that they had only 1½ pence between them. David showed it to the conductor.

'That's all we've got,' he said.

'I said that'll be another two pence,' repeated the conductor slowly.

'But we haven't got any more money,' said David anxiously.

'Come on,' said the conductor, it's another two pence.'

'But how can we give you another two pence when we haven't got two pence,' said David. He looked out of the window. 'Anyway we're getting off here.'

'Give me two pence,' said the conductor, his voice even louder.

'Look,' said David, 'we'll give you our names and addresses and you can send for it, or we'll get off.'

'It's another two pence,' came the strong reply.

David had had enough. If the conductor wasn't going to take his name and address then he was getting off. There was no sense in arguing.

'Alright,' he said, 'we'll get off.' David and Geoff stood up and went to walk towards the stairs. The bus conductors hand shot out and he grabbed hold of David's arm. 'I'm not having that" thought David. He tried to break the conductors' grip. Geoff watched what was happening and shouted.

'Leave him alone.' He tried to get the conductors' hand off of David. The conductor pushed Geoff back on to the seat and banged down on the floor with his heel to signal the driver to come up. 'I bet the driver's a dirty great bloke, or the conductor wouldn't have done anything. I'm getting out of here', thought David. He broke the conductors' hold and held his arm. His left foot shot out to the back of the conductor's right heel, David brought his foot back again and the conductor, forced to stand on one foot, lost his balance and fell over.

'Come on,' shouted David. 'Run.' The two boys ran down the stairs and jumped off the bus. The conductor ran down to the platform and shouted and began to swear. David looked at Geoff, and noticed he was rubbing his leg.

'What happened?' he asked.

'As I ran past him the bastard kicked me, he had dirty great winkle pickers on.' For the first time since David had met Geoff he lost his temper.

'I'll kill him for that,' he shouted.

The bus had stopped at the lights and was waiting for them to change. Geoff started to run towards it. But David realised that if Geoff hit the conductor then he could get into serious trouble with the police. David grabbed hold of Geoff from behind in a type of bear hug. 'Don't be an idiot,' he shouted. But Geoff just ignored him and kept trying to get over to the conductor who was watching everything from the platform of the bus. David had held much bigger boys than Geoff at judo but he had never known anybody to have such a violent temper. David could only hold Geoff for about ten seconds until Geoff broke away and ran over to the bus.

'Get off that fucking bus,' he shouted from the pavement.

David watched from about 25 yards up the road and noticed that the conductor was beginning to get frightened.

'Calm down, son,' David heard him say. 'Come on, come here and we'll talk it over.' Geoff moved towards the platform. David could see the conductors foot move into the position to kick out.

'Watch his foot,' he shouted. Geoff moved back just in time to see the foot of the conductor shoot out towards his face. The burning desire to hit the conductor mounted inside Geoff. He ran over to the milk crate that was up against the wall and picked up an empty bottle. When he turned around the bus had driven away from the lights. Geoff threw down the bottle in anger and it smashed on the pavement. The crowd that had gathered slowly dispersed.

David ran up to Geoff. He looked at the fire in Geoff's eyes.

'If I ever see him again,' said Geoff, 'I'll kill him.'

'Yes,' said David, watching the bus disappear round the corner, 'so will I. Come on, let's go home.'

'Com'on,' said Mr. Pitfield the next morning. 'Yer been here five minutes and yer haven't done a stroke of work yet.' Geoff was given the job of pushing a whole side of bacon into the freezer and it was very difficult. Now that there was no tutorial class during the holidays, Geoff was working at Penrights full time. This way he was paid six pounds a week. It was now three weeks into the holidays and Geoff had made his mind up. He was going to leave Penrights after the six week holiday. The the manager was standing around joking with one of the delivery men as they watched Geoff struggle to get the heavy bacon side into the freezer.

'What was the donkey doing down Soho?' Mr Pitfield asked as he offered the man a sweet.

'Looking for a 'ASS PRO,' he laughed. Geoff gave a heave and the bacon thundered into the other joints in the freezer. He looked at his hands. They were red with salt and other preservatives that were put onto the bacon.

'Just before I leave,' he said to himself, 'I'm going to put some Exlax in the manager's tea.' He laughed inwardly. Suddenly a man wearing a blue overall came down the stairs.

'Eggs,' he shouted waving an order form. Geoff stood at the bottom of the conveyor belt as Pitfield loaded on box after box of eggs. After all the eggs were stacked away in the corner one of the other shop assistants shouted down for some articles she wanted up. She sent the list down and Geoff sent up the stock. And that was how it went on. Delivery after delivery, work after work and not much money to show for it. The Monday after,

Geoff and David decided that, as there was no judo for David because of the holiday, they would ride around on their bicycles.

It was about 8 o'clock when they set out after David had had an unexpected visit from Michael on his bicycle. David introduced Geoff to Michael and they started out. They had just ridden past the Bank of England when suddenly a policeman stepped out into the road in front of them. They pulled over into the kerb.

'Where's your light?' he snapped at Michael.

'It's broken, it's at home,' answered Michael.

'That's no excuse,' growled the policeman, 'you should always have a front light.' He looked at the boys and then at the bicycles.

'What make is your bike?' he asked Michael.

'What colour is it?' Michael looked down at the bicycle.

'Don't look down,' snapped the policeman.

'It's red,' came the answer. The policeman passed onto Geoff.

'What make is your bike?' he asked.

'Tarmaster,' answered Geoff.

'What colour are your mudguards?' Geoff looked at the mudguards, then at the policeman.

'Red,' he answered.

'What make are your brakes? And don't look down this time.' Geoff looked down. 'Look bonehead,' shouted the policeman, 'I told you not to look down.' Geoff was feeling very angry now, all the boys were. They didn't like being talked to in that manner.

'Well,' said Geoff sarcastically, 'I'm not in the habit of taking a guided tour around my bike.' The policeman sneered and walked up to David.

'What make is your bike,' he snapped.

'I don't know,' answered David who had decided that it was best not to be sarcastic. 'I think its a co-op.'

'You think,' shouted the policeman. 'Don't you know?'

'Well,' answered David. 'It's not my bike, it's my brother's but he doesn't use it any more.'

'A likely story,' remarked the policeman.

'You know what I think?' he said to all three of them. 'I think you've nicked these bikes. Because you haven't given sufficient evidence that they are yours.'

'Of course we have,' said Geoff.

'Look, don't give me that shit,' snapped the policeman, 'because I don't want to know. You can tell it all to the sergeant at the station.'

Geoff shrugged his shoulders. It was no use, he was going to take them to the police station anyway. The policeman unclipped the two way radio from his breast pocket, brought it up to his mouth and pressed a button. There was a crackling noise and then a loud metallic voice spoke. The boys couldn't make out what it was saying, but they could hear the policeman's reply.

'I've got three juveniles here. I suspect that they've stolen some bikes. Can you send a van round?'

The voice answered. The policeman clipped the radio onto his pocket.

'Right,' he said with a grin. 'You can tell your story to the sergeant and God help you if these bikes are nicked.'

A few seconds later a blue police transit van followed by a panda car came whizzing round the corner and pulled up in front of the boys.

'They wouldn't have been so quick if we'd just mugged someone,' thought George. He smiled inwardly as the two policemen in the van and the one from the panda got out and walked over to them. They said something to the policeman and then got back into the van and panda.

'Alright,' said the policeman opening the doors of the van. 'Put the bikes in and then sit down.'

David, Geoff and Michael put the bicycles in and sat down on the long seat. The policeman got in and slammed the door shut. The van pulled out into the road. The policeman looked at the boys.

'Look,' he said. 'You'll find me a bundle of laughs if you're telling the truth. But if I have any flash answers, then there are going to be a few thick ears. Understand?'

The boys nodded. The van rolled down to the car park below the station, the boys got out and put their bicycles up against the wall.

'Not there, for God's sake!' exclaimed the policeman. 'That's the chief inspector's parking space. You leave your bikes there and you'll get the electric chair.'

The policeman laughed, and the boys, hoping to get on the good side of him forced themselves to laugh too. He pointed to another space and the boys put their machines there.

They were shown up to the first floor and along a corridor to a door. The policeman knocked on the door and through the window David, Geoff and Michael could see another policeman, who was carrying a bunch of keys, come over and look through the window. He unlocked the door and the boys went in and were told to sit on a long wooden bench in the corner of the room. The policeman locked the door and strolled over to the desk at the other side of the room where a man was being questioned. His face was covered with blood and he was shaking. The policeman who was questioning the man started shouting at him as the policeman that had stopped the boys came back and knelt down in front of them on one knee and balanced a piece of paper on the other.

'Now,' he said looking at David. 'What's your name?'

'David Philip Cook,' came the answer.

'How old are you, Dave?'

'Fourteen.'

'And your address?'

'78 Little Turner Street, London, E.1.'

'And where were you born, David?' came the next question.

David was puzzled. Why was the policeman being so nice suddenly? Perhaps it was because he realised that the bikes were theirs.

'The East End Maternity Hospital,' he answered.

'Is the bike that you're riding yours?'

'No, it's my brother's.'

The policeman passed on to Geoff and asked him the same questions, and he did the same when he came to Michael. Then he stood up and walked over to a door and called Geoff, David and Michael in. It was a very small room. In the corner was a table and by the door was a height measure.

'Right,' said the policeman, 'let's check your heights.'

David stood in front of the 8 foot stick and the policeman marked down his height on a piece of paper.

'5 foot 8 inches,' he said. He then did the same to Michael.

'5 foot 7 inches,' he wrote down. He turned to Geoff.

'Looks like you're going to be the short arse,' he laughed and measured Geoff.

'5 foot 4 inches,' he said. The boys were then taken back into the charge room.

Opposite them sat three policemen; one on a chair and two on a desk. The policeman on the chair called over a policewoman.

'Ere, Sue,' he said, 'take a look at them three.'

He pointed to the boys. The policewoman smiled.

'Have you ever seen a tougher looking bunch of bike thieves than those before? I'd say they'll get the electric chair for this, wouldn't you?'

She nodded and walked out of the room.

'They're so sure,' whispered David.

'Yeah,' said Geoff. 'They're practically having bets on whether we nicked them or not.'

The boys quietly chuckled.

'Any minute now,' said Michael softly, 'honest policeman Plod will bring out a tote board and start chalking down the odds.'

'It's going to break their hearts when they find out we haven't nicked them,' thought Geoff.

'You know what,' said one of the policeman sitting on the table. 'These three fit the description of those blokes that did that bank' he laughed.

A sergeant came into the room and stood looking down at the boys.

'Now' he said, 'the reason you are here is that you could not prove that the bikes you were riding were yours. So therefore we must have our doubts as to whether or not those bikes are your property. We've checked the serial number of the bikes and we're now going to compare them with the serial numbers of all the stolen bikes in the records at Scotland Yard, and if the serial numbers are not in the records then I can only say we're sorry for any inconvenience we've caused you. But if the same serial numbers are in the records at Scotland Yard then you will appear in front of a Juvenile Court. Do you understand?' The boys nodded. 'Now then,' he said, 'if you would like to go upstairs with the constable that brought you in then you can wait while we're checking the records.' They were shown upstairs into another charge room. This time there was nobody in the room except for two policewomen.

The policeman opened one of the two thick iron doors with little square peep holes in it and gestured that the boys should go in.

'Just wait here a minute' he said. He went out and the boys heard two bolts draw across the door and a key turned in the lock. The boys looked around. It was a fairly big detention room. About 6 feet up the wall there was a double glazed frosted window that had no use as far as the boys could see except for taking a little strip of pale yellow light into the room, that nobody could ever possibly read in. On the ceiling was a small square piece of glass with a bulb behind it. David thought it looked a bit like a microphone. The boys, for the first time since they had gone into the station, were frightened. In the charge room where a lot of people were walking in and out it was not frightening, but in this big empty, cold room it was completely different especially as they were locked in. For a few seconds David had the same sickening feeling as when he was in Wallington College and could not get away; he shook it off by talking.

'Cosy here isn't it' he said, glad to hear his voice in the emptiness of the room.

David sat down and rested his chin in his hands.

'And there was I', he said miserably, 'thinking that all policemen were soft-hearted little goody-goodies.'

'So did I,' remarked Michael.

'And that shows how wrong we were,' said Geoff.

Walking over to the door, he looked through the peephole. and saw nothing. The small wooden shutter was drawn over it blocking all view.

David told Geoff and Michael about the light that looked like a microphone. Geoff looked up.

'If that is a microphone,' he said softly, 'and somebody is listening then I'm sorry for all the trouble we've caused.'

'On the other hand, if that isn't a microphone then I think old Policeman Plod that brought us in should have half a ton of ex-lax put in his tea.'

'Yeah,' said David, 'did you see the way he was looking at you, Geoff' Michael laughed even more.

'I thought he was gonna kill you,' he said.

'Yeah, he is a tough nut,' commented David.

All three of them laughed. Michael lay down on the bench with his hands behind his head and looked around the room.

'How about,' he smiled, 'if we got all our mates and loads of beer in here and a record player. We could have a party in here then.' David was feeling better now.

'You can just imagine,' he said, 'one of the coppers opening the door and he finds 50 odd people in here and music playing and a load of party streamers are flying about.'

'Yeah,' said Michael excitedly, 'then we can go over to him and say 'come in my old son, have a drink'...you can just imagine his face.

After an hour and a half the boys got quite used to the place until David was called out by one of the policemen. He locked the door after him.

The first person David saw was his father sitting in the charge room. David was asked to sign his name in a book.' 'Just for the record' and then he was taken home by his father after the police said that they had checked the record and David was 'clear'. It was 10.45 when the door was opened again. This time Michael was shown out to the charge room where his father was waiting to collect him. Geoff was left on his own. It was no longer a 'laugh'. He knocked on the door.

'Can I go to the toilet,' he shouted.

'You'll be going home soon,' answered a policeman in the charge room. Geoff sat down again in the gloomy   detaining room and thought. He thought about starting Selton. And he wondered if he would settle down there. And he thought of Penright and how hard it was carrying heavy boxes and having hardly any money at the end of the week to show for it. He remembered the day after he had started and how he told David how 'great' it was. 'I was a right silly moo' he thought. He had made up his mind.

'I'm gonna leave at the end of the week,' he told himself.

He heard someone shouting outside the charge room and a shuffling of feet. He jumped up and looked out of the peep hole, where he saw two policemen dragging a huge coloured woman over to a bench opposite Geoff's detention room. A third policeman staggered into view being nursed by a policewoman, his face covered in blood.

The woman was bundled into the corner behind a table and two policemen sat either side of her. She was going completely mad. She was screaming and swearing. It took the policemen all their strength to hold her. A sergeant came running over.

'You'd better put her in one of the rooms,' he said. The policewoman came over to Geoff's detaining room and unlocked the door. Geoff, not wishing to appear nosey sat down quietly, in the corner. The policewoman opened the door a little and peeped in. She could not see Geoff in the corner.

'There's nobody in here,' she said, 'bring her over.'

Geoff had never been so terrified in all his life. He felt his heart skip a beat as they brought 6 foot 4 inches of mad woman over to the detaining room. He was on the point of screaming the place down in order to let them know that he was in the room when suddenly one of the policemen shouted:

'Hold it, there's a boy in there, put her in the next room.'

Geoff breathed a sigh of relief.

'Thank God,' he said. The door opened and the policeman that brought him in asked Geoff to go out to the charge-room. He sat down opposite a policeman at the desk.

'We've checked your bike', he said clicking his pen, 'And you were telling the truth'. After a little chat about how to keep on the good side of the police, Geoff was told he could go home. Geoff was not on the phone so the police decided to take Geoff and his bike home in a van and then they could get a constable to explain everything that had happened to Geoff's parents personally. Geoff said goodbye and he was then taken home.

The Saturday after, Geoff was in Penrights piling up trolleys and baskets inside the shop. The shop was only closing for a week and while everyone except Geoff was upstairs getting their cards, Mr Pitfield was going through the fridge for some frozen food that he would not have to pay for. Geoff wondered if he should tell Mr Pitfield that he was leaving and decided against it. He would let Mr Pitfield get on with all the unloading himself on the Monday after the holiday.

'Sod the whole shop', he thought.

In one week he would be starting Selton, so that was enough to worry about. He had gone for the interview just before the holidays and he knew a little about the school.

'Starting Selton', he thought. He remembered his dizzy spells and his agrophobia and wondered if they would start all over again. He shrugged his shoulders and picked the next basket up.

CHAPTER 9

HERE WE GO AGAIN

'I wonder what it's gonna be like', thought Geoff as he walked along Cartridge Street towards Selton. His stomach turned over when he walked through the black iron gates and into the playground. It was a very old establishment built around 1880. A playground stretched all the way round it like a huge concrete moat expanding at one end into a small football pitch, then narrowly streaming out to the other side into a smaller play area. Geoff wondered how he would react to the school. Still, the good thing was if he ever came over dizzy, he wouldn't have far to go if he ran home, which was just down the road about half a mile from the school. He had started off at his new school on the wrong foot by being ten minutes late. As he went through the gates directly opposite him on the far wall of the playground was a mural consisting of white silhouettes of people on a bench; they were running about catching coloured balls whilst dogs were licking little children's ice-creams. Geoff thought it was rather a silly mural.

Geoff opened a door of the building and began climbing the stairs. There were two staircases that ran parallel at opposite ends of the school. On the first floor where all the classrooms were, stood a stage in a big assembly hall. On the next floor was the headmaster's office and the staff room and, on the top floor were the woodwork room and art room. On the other side was the cookery class and the smaller children's class. Geoff reached the first floor and gingerly walked towards the register room which faced the hall. As the population of the school was only fifty children and eight teachers, they never used the assembly hall. Geoff had always feared being in a hall or a classroom when everyone had to be quiet and he would sit in his chair and know that if he became dizzy he would not be able to get out without everyone looking at him, or the teacher calling him back and asking him in front of all the school why he wanted to go out. Geoff breathed deeply and opened the door of the register room. The headmaster stopped calling the names out when he saw everybody in the room look in the direction of the door.

'Sorry I'm late', said Geoff strolling into the room.

'That's OK Geoff', said Mr Reed the headmaster, 'Sit down somewhere'. He pointed to a seat in the front and Geoff sat down. Mr Reed continued reading the register. Suddenly there was a scream from the back of the room. The whole class looked in the direction of the scream, where a boy and girl were sitting next to each other. The boy hit the girl (she was coloured) and the girl retaliated by hitting the boy around the head with all her strength. Suddenly from the other side of the room a tall bearded teacher rushed over, kicking a chair over in the process and grabbed hold of the girl.

'Let me go', she screamed. Still holding the girl, the man asked the boy what was wrong.

'The bastard kept digging me in the back', bellowed the girl before the boy could answer.

As big as he was, the teacher was still having a lot of trouble holding the girl. She kept screaming and shouting for about fifteen minutes. In fact she lost her temper so much that she had to be held down on the floor by the teacher, Mr Hamilton. Mr Reed started the name calling ceremony again. He managed to read out two names before the coloured girl started shouting and swearing again. This time she had to be taken outside by Mr Hamilton. Mr Reed turned to Geoff, 'Don't let that worry you', he said, 'it's just one of Sheila's moods. She's not always like that'.

Geoff gave a nod. It did worry him; in fact it worried him a lot. He knew that the children were noisy, but he didn't know tantrums were everyday things. 'But then again', he thought, 'that means that if I have a dizzy spell, I'll be able to go out so it's not so bad after all'.

Mr Reed finished the assembly with a few words about the new term and arranged all fifty children into some kind of a decent timetable, all the classes had roughly seven children to a class. Mrs Cole took the children from eleven to thirteen, Mr Watts took the children from seven to ten. Mr Hamilton's class consisted of children Geoff's age or a bit older. The art mistress was a woman called Mrs Buckley. A teacher called Mr Walker took the children for woodwork. There was also two other teachers but Geoff was told to go along with Mr Hamilton to his new class.

Mr Hamilton led Geoff and six other boys along the hall and into a classroom near the stairs. 'OK', he said, opening the door. 'You lot get in here', and Mr Hamilton locked the door behind them all. Geoff asked a tall very thin boy with short brown hair, 'Why's he locking the door?' 'Don't let that worry yer', said the boy, 'it's not to keep us in, it's to keep the other kids out because a lot of them wander about the school messing up the classes, so this way it stops them coming in here'. Geoff forced a smile but he didn't care much for the locked door. Supposing he came over dizzy? The boy kept talking. 'When I first came here', he said, 'I didn't like the idea of it', he gestured towards the door, 'but I got used to it'.

'How long have you been here?' asked Geoff.

'About a month'.

'Why were you sent here?'

The boy brushed the question aside by saying, 'It's a long story', and walking over to a chair in the corner.

Geoff looked around the room. Like all the other rooms in the school, the ceiling was very high up. There was not much furniture, just three tables and a few chairs and a small book shelf. The whole room, like the whole school, was painted dark brown and white. While Geoff and the boy had been talking, the other boys just wandered around the room while Mr Hamilton sat at a table reading something. Geoff noticed that all the boys were sitting on the tables and not the chairs. He walked over to the thin boy. 'Doesn't anyone here sit on chairs?' he asked. The boy laughed, 'What chairs?'

Geoff looked round the room and realised what the laughter meant; there were only three chairs and all except for one of them were broken. Mr Hamilton stood up and came over to Geoff.

'Well', he said, 'I suppose I'd better introduce you to everybody'. He pointed to the thin boy. 'This is Ian', he said. He introduced the six other boys. Geoff sat down next to Ian.

'You still haven't told me why you're here', he asked.

'It's a long story', said Ian, 'but I'll make it short'. He folded his arms and looked at Geoff.

'It all started when I left primary school', he said. 'I just couldn't stand the secondary school I was sent to. I couldn't bear to be in it. I just had to get out'.

'Yeah', interrupted Geoff, 'I know what you mean'.

'Well, anyway', said Ian, 'they took me out of that school because I kept bunking off and they put me in another school. But it was just the same. Once I even nicked one of the teachers' motor bikes to get away quick. He'd left it in the playground and it was break, and there were two prefects standing around near the gate, so I jumped on the bike but the teacher came out and caught me before I had a chance to start it. So I was expelled and sent to another school, but I kept running away from that and then the school doctor said I should see a psychiatrist and the psychiatrist said I should leave the school and go to a tutorial class—a tutorial class is where . . .'

'Yeah, I know', said Geoff.

'Oh', said Ian, 'so I went to a tutorial for about five months and then I was sent here. And I've been here for a month and I've only bunked off twice', he smiled.

Geoff told Ian of his troubles at school. After about twenty minutes Mr Hamilton went over to the door and unlocked it. Ian picked up a football from underneath one of the tables and walked over to the door.

'Come on', he shouted to Geoff. 'We're gonna have a game of football'.

'Don't we do any work?' asked Geoff as he walked down   the stairs.

'Yeah, sometimes', answered Ian. The boys arranged a five a side football match with some of the smaller children that were wandering around the playground.

'Have we got a football team? Geoff asked Ian.

'Yeah', he replied, 'I haven't had a chance to play in it yet 'cos I started in July and the football season starts next month.

Geoff and Ian worked well. As a two-man team they were both good players and they loved football.

A very tall thin girl with long jet black hair sat on the bench watching the game.

'Who's that?' asked Geoff.

'Who? Her?' enquired Ian, nodding towards the girl who was about the same age as himself and Geoff. 'That's Teresa Doves'.

Geoff gave a sly smile. 'Does she er . . well you know?' he asked.

'No, not really', answered Ian. He turned and ran after the ball.

Mr Hamilton blew his whistle after five minutes.

'Oh, come on Hamilton, just another hour'.

The boys were shepherded up the stairs to the classroom.

Upstairs for art, Mrs Buckley was busy laying the table with paper and paint as the boys strolled into the classroom.

'Where are the others?' she asked, looking up from a table.

'Steve, Bill and Barry are around somewhere and the rest have gone to the cafe round the market', answered Ian. Geoff and Ian sat down and began to paint.

'I'm glad you two aren't as noisy as the rest of them', said Mrs Buckley.

'Yeah, well we're sophisticated', smiled Ian. 'Come on', he laughed. 'let's have yer clothes off girl so I can paint yer in the nude'.

They did not get to paint Mrs Buckley in the nude but they did manage to paint a pot of flowers which were now dead as they hadn't been watered through the holidays.

Geoff settled down quite well with the people and the surroundings of Selton. He did not experience any dizzy spells and they seemed to have left him, but he still thought about them although it didn't worry him so much.

'It's a pity David's not here', Geoff thought as he was playing football one Thursday afternoon. 'I could have had a laugh here with him and I bet Ian would like him too'.

He ran up the playground and tried to get the ball from Mr Hamilton.

CHAPTER 10

TARGET: THE OLYMPICS

That afternoon Geoff went round to see David, not knowing that he would be spending the evening in a Judo suit. Geoff knocked on David's door around about four o'clock in the afternoon. A few seconds later David opened the door.

'Hello', said Geoff, 'I've just come from Selton and I thought I'd come and brighten up your dull uneventful life'.

Geoff looked for the smile on David's face that normally came when Geoff was being witty, but instead of a smile there was only a worried look. Geoff sensed there was something not quite right and asked 'What's wrong?'

'Come on in and I'll tell you', said David. Geoff walked in and closed the door behind him, then the two boys went into the ground floor room that David and his brothers used for talking to their friends and playing records. Geoff sat down on a settee and David sat opposite him on a long cushion that stretched the length of the wall.

'Do you remember that time up at the tutorial class when you found out about Selton?' asked the worried David.

'Yeah' said Geoff. 'What of it?'

'Well', continued David, 'I said that I wasn't that unlucky to go to Selton. Well I am'.

Geoff looked surprised. 'What do you mean?' he asked.

'I had an appointment with Dr Chamber, my psychiatrist, this afternoon. So I went up there and he said that as I was doing so well at Mrs Cox's, he had decided that I should go to another school. Not a normal one but one that would help me overcome my problems. I asked which one and he said Selton and that he would make an appointment for my mum and dad to see him with me and he said that he wanted me to go for an interview. So tomorrow a letter'll come saying when my mum and dad should go and see him. And if they all agree, then I'll probably be going to Selton', he sighed.

'So what's wrong with that?' asked Geoff.

'I can't bear being in a normal school, so how will I be able to go to a loony-bin like Selton?'

'It's not a loony-bin', said Geoff, 'it's just that some of the kids have got problems that a normal school can't cope with'.

'You're sounding like Dr Chambers now', said David.

The noise of the front door slamming vibrated through the house. The door opened and Stephen came into the room and dropped his briefcase onto the floor.

'You should have seen the bird I was squeezed up against on the bus just now', he said. 'She had the biggest pair of knockers you've ever seen.' He sat down on the settee.

'I beg your pardon', laughed David.

'Look', smiled Stephen, 'if you didn't get it the first time, then I'm not going to repeat myself'.

He looked at Geoff and then at David. 'I see he's here again', smiled Stephen, nodding at Geoff. 'When's he moving in?'

'Tomorrow, if you don't shut up', said Geoff.

Stephen took his blazer off and hung it up. 'What are yer doing tonight?' he asked Geoff.

'Why?'

'Because if yer not doing anything, why don't yer come to Judo? We could do with some new people'.

'Yeah', said David. 'Why not?'

'Because for one reason I'm no good at it'.

'I was no good when I first started', said Stephen.

'Girls', remarked David.

'What?' asked Geoff.

'There are two girls over at the club. Angela and Kim. I used to go to school with Angela's brother, he was in my class and that's how I got to know her. I knowed her for years'.

'If yer going to talk about her', interrupted Stephen, 'then I'm going upstairs'. He walked out of the room and shut the door.

'What did he mean by that?' enquired Geoff.

'Nothing', said David, 'He was just trying to be funny. Anyway, seeing as I know her, we should have no trouble chatting them up'.

Geoff's face brightened up. 'All right', he said, 'what time do you want me round?'

'About half six with a towel and a pair of trunks to wear underneath your suit in case yer trousers fall down'.

Geoff called for David at half past six and he, David and Stephen set off for Judo. Geoff was shown into a large rest room. At one end of the room was a counter where you could buy orange drinks and items like that; next to that was a small office. In the opposite corner was a television and behind it stretching all along the wall were several doors that opened into a large cupboard. The cupboard contained rows and rows of Judo suits that the club lent out to people that wanted to do Judo but had no suits. The cupboard was so big a person could walk about in it selecting suits. Around the room were also several tables and chairs.

David told Geoff that if he wanted to do Judo he had to

enroll as a member of the club. To do this, Geoff had to see the club's 'boss-man' as Stephen called him — Mr Pollock. David took Geoff into the rest room and then into the office. Mr Pollock was talking on the telephone. He put the phone down and asked David what he wanted.

'This is Geoff,' said David. 'And he wants to be the next world champion at Judo.'

Mr Pollock smiled. 'Does he!' he said. 'Well I suppose I had better enroll him then.'

Mr Pollock took out a large register from his desk, took Geoff's name and address and twenty-five pence, the club's subs for a term.

David took Geoff over to the cupboard and they took out a suit about Geoff's size. David said that he would probably look silly as all the Judo suits in the club were large sizes.

For the first time since Geoff had come in, he noticed two girls sitting by a table; he told David.

'That's Angela and Kim,' said David. 'Let's go over to them, we've still got a few minutes till the class starts.'

He walked over to them and sat down next to Angela. David introduced Geoff. They sat talking for about ten minutes until George came into the room.

'Here he is,' said Kim distastefully, 'Marvel Mist himself.'

George casually strolled over to a chair next to a table, stepping on someone's foot in the process. He turned the chair round and sat on it with his elbows resting on the back of the chair just the way he had seen the cowboys do in all the best cowboy films. He noticed a can of cola on the table.

'Watcha girls,' he said, slowly lifting the can up to his lips and then blushing when he saw it was empty.

David looked at his watch. 'Come on girls,' he said, 'time we got changed.'

He shouted over to George to get a Judo suit. George stood up, walked over to the cupboard and disappeared behind the doors.

'If there's one thing I can't stand,' said Angela looking in the direction of the wardrobe, 'it's a big-head, and a smelly one at that.'

Geoff and David started laughing. There was a loud 'thud' as something banged against the cupboard door from the inside — all eyes turned in George's direction as he staggered from the cupboard rubbing his head.

'Bloody hell,' was the only word he managed to say before everyone in the room burst out laughing.

'What happened?' asked David.

'I was tugging at a suit that was caught in a hanger and I pulled it so hard I fell backwards and bashed me head on the door.'

The bellow of laughter could still be heard from the girls' changing room as the three boys walked into their changing room. George changed in silence and quickly went downstairs to the gymnasium. When David and Geoff came down everybody but the girls had changed and were 'loosening up'. Geoff had had a lot of trouble with his belt as they are very complicated to do up. Geoff looked at David for some reassurance as he got onto the mat. David started rolling around on the mat.

'What yer doing?' said Geoff.

'I'm loosening up,' said David. 'Because when you first come on to the mat you're all stiff, and if you're stiff, then you can't do Judo any good.'

'Oh, I see,' said Geoff.

Suddenly there was the sound of laughter from the other side of the mat. It was Stephen.

'What's so funny?' asked Geoff.

'It's your Judo suit,' said Stephen, 'it's about ten times too big for you. Can I get in with you? You must be lonely.'

Geoff looked down at his suit. It was indeed too big for him. The trousers that were supposed to reach the top of his shoes were so long that he nearly tripped over every time he walked. And his jacket that was made so the sleeves hung down to a few inches past his elbows, hung down way past his knuckles. And the ends of his belt hung down to his knees. Geoff was rather put off Judo because of the suit. He had thought that he would look like James Bond and not a bundle of laundry.

Mr Jones came over and started to teach Geoff the breakfalls as he had to learn how to fall before he could learn how to throw. David meanwhile was practising some throws with Michael. After about an hour of rolling one way and then the other, Geoff was shown how to do a throw called Tiaotoshi. This baffled Geoff; he just couldn't get the hang of the weird Japanese phrases and names.

At about 8.15 Mr Jones told everybody that it was time for Randories. Geoff had only learnt the basics of one throw but Mr Jones said it was all right for David to have a randorie as long as he went slowly and gently. Everybody faced each other as partners. Mr Jones said 'Rai', everyone bowed and the Randorie began. David gave Geoff a few minutes to sort out how to hold, his left hand in David's right sleeve and his right hand on David's left lapel.

After about half an hour of Geoff falling over as soon as David touched him and Geoff flying through the air in every Randorie, the class finally came to an end. The boys got changed and went home after Geoff had told David that he wouldn't go again and that he would stick to football — it was safer.

The next morning David's father received a letter from Dr Chambers saying that he would like to discuss David going to Selton with them on Friday at 11 o'clock.

The following Friday David found himself sitting in front of Dr Chambers with his mother and father. They talked for about an hour in which David realised that if he didn't go to Selton he would still have to go to another school.

'Anyway,' said the doctor, 'you'll only go until you've overcome your fear and then, who knows, we may be able to get you back to a proper school.' David had to agree. What could he do? Where else could he go? The doctor said David had made the right decision and that he would phone Mr Reed up that afternoon and in a few days they would probably get a letter saying when they should go for an interview.

David and his parents said goodbye to Dr Chambers and went home. There was still one last chance thought David. With some luck he may not be accepted.

CHAPTER 11

INTERVIEW

A few days later a letter arrived from Selton stating that an interview had been arranged for the following Tuesday. This worried David as he thought that he would have at least six weeks before the interview so he would not have to worry about it for a while. David always thought it strange how fast time flew when he didn't want it to. He would like to have made time stand still so that the day of the interview would never come. But time never stood still and that feared Tuesday morning came closer and closer until before David knew it, he was getting washed and ready to meet Mr Reed, the headmaster of Selton.

At 10.45 (the interview was at 11) David, his mother and father set out for Selton. They walked through the gates and were confronted by a small boy who directed them to the head-master's office. They followed the boy up to the second floor and David's father knocked on the door which was opened by a fairly young woman, about thirty four with short black hair. There were two other people in the room besides the woman. A youngish man with thick black hair and black horn-rimmed spectacles, and a middle-aged woman with long brown hair. She also wore spectacles. The man got up from behind a desk in the far corner of the room and walked round to David's mother and father and shook hands with them. He introduced himself as Mr Reed and he introduced the two other people in the room. The woman that had opened the door was his secretary Mrs Young and the other woman was Dr Garish, the school psychiatrist. David and his parents sat down. It was a comfortable room; a small gas fire stood in a bricked-in fireplace, next to the door was another desk and round the room were several cabinets containing books. In the centre of the room were five chairs in a small circle.

Mr Reed sat down facing Mr Cook, next to him sat the psychiatrist and then Mrs Cook and David; the secretary Mrs Young sat behind her desk near the door.

'Well,' said Mr Reed, 'I've read David's school report. It tells me a lot but I'd prefer to hear all about his troubles at school from you and David.' He looked at David; 'Well, will you tell me?' he asked. David just mumbled something like, 'I don't know,' and then looked at his parents. He didn't like the look of this school. Ever since he had come through the gates, his stomach had been turning over and over, and she felt quite sick. In fact he wished he could get up and run out of the terrible place and never go back again. 'Why did I ever have to come here?' he thought. At the tutorial class he had been safe. It was quiet and peaceful there, but in this old dark school where the children rushed about screaming, shouting and fighting, he just didn't know what to do; he would have liked to run away and hide. The answer to Mr Reed's question was supplied by Mrs Cook.

'I suppose it all started,' she said, 'when David left his primary school. You see he always wanted to go to his brother Stephen's school.'

'He's the next one up from David, isn't he?' interrupted Mr Reed.

'Yes,' answered Mrs Cook. 'Anyway, the headmaster of David's primary school said that as Stephen's school is a grammar school, he didn't think it was suitable for David, as he might not be able to keep up with the other boys.' Mrs Cook then told Mr Reed of the trouble David had at all his schools. And Mr Reed and the psychiatrist occasionally asked a question. Dr Garish then asked David if he would like to go down to her office where he could tell her his side of the story. David agreed. He didn't want to do anything except go home but, as that was impossible, David reluctantly followed Dr Garish down to the first floor. Directly opposite the stairs was a cloakroom and next to it was a door. Dr Garish walked over to the door and unlocked it. There were three doors in a circle; one right in front of them and one on the right of them and one one the left.

David walked in and the psychiatrist locked the door. 'This is Lawrence Dane's room, he's the psychotherapist. You'll be meeting him,' she said pointing to the door on the left of the circle. She pointed to the door on the right hand. 'And that's the medical room.' She took out a bunch of keys from her bag. 'And this,' she said, opening the middle door, 'is my room.'

David walked in and sat down on one of the two armchairs that were up against the wall next to a desk. It was a very small room. Behind David was a small filing cabinet, on the desk stood a telephone and a few books. Dr Garish pulled her chair in front of David and looked at him. David felt uncomfortable and very nervous. He avoided the doctor's gaze and stared at the telephone.

'Now David,' she said, 'do you think you can tell me why you don't want to go to school?' David was feeling very self-conscious and he brushed all the questions aside with an 'I don't know', or 'yes' or 'maybe'. After about an hour the doctor seemed to give up all hope of getting a proper answer from David. She said, 'I've got to go upstairs for a minute. You'll be alright here on your own will you?' David nodded and the psychiatrist walked out of the room locking the door behind her.

David gazed round the room. He walked over to the small window that overlooked the playground and looked out of it. He did not like the school, he did not like the atmosphere or the children except Geoff. It was true that he hadn't really met any of them but he just didn't like the noise they made and all their shouting and rushing around. There were only fifty children but they seemed to make more noise than a thousand. 'No,' he thought, 'I'm definitely not staying here.'

There was a knock on the door. He turned round and looked through the glass square in the door. A well built boy of about fifteen years shouted through the door.

'Open the door, will yer mate?' he asked.

'I can't, I haven't got the key.'

The boy sneered at David and said, 'liar'; he turned and walked away.

David sat down again on one of the chairs. 'This is a right mess,' he thought. 'If only I had gone to Stephen's school, all this would have never happened. He was still thinking of the events of the previous two years when the psychiatrist came into the room.

'The headmaster wants you back upstairs,' she said. David got up and walked back upstairs to the office with Dr Garish. He went in and sat down.'

'Now David,' said Mr Reed, 'we had a long talk with your parents and it seems to me that you're a very quiet sort of boy and I'm not really certain if this school is suitable as the children are so noisy and robust. So I'm going to talk it over with the teachers and see what they think and then I'll let you know in a few days. All right?'

David and his parents said goodbye to Mr Reed and left. All the way home David thought maybe they would not accept him. At least, if that happened (because the council took such a long time over everything) he'd probably be at home for about the next six months.

A few days later another letter arrived from Selton. This time it had David's worst fear in it. *He had been accepted*, and he was to go on the following Friday. 'Friday,' thought David. 'That's just one week away.' He hardly had time to think what he was going to do. It also said in the letter that they thought Friday was the best day as then it could be a sort of 'practice' day and he could see how the school ran before he went for a whole week.

The following Friday dawned bright and sunny. But not for

David. Every time he had thought of this morning during the past week, he had shivered and his stomach had turned over. He washed, dressed and had breakfast, trying all the time not to think of Selton. He looked at the clock. It was 9.15. Time to go.

'Now you're sure you don't want me to walk down there with you to help you settle in?' asked David's mother, as he walked down the stairs.

'No, it's all right Mum, I'll get there,' he said.

He walked out of the house and shut the door. 'Who am I kidding?' he thought as he walked round the corner. 'I probably won't get there. I never will.'

Selton was only up the road from David's house so he did not have far to go. A few minutes later he was standing outside the gates.

'Should I go in or not?' he thought. 'Christ, what am I going to do?' He stood there, just staring at the gates and listening to the two sides of him arguing 'go in or run? go in or run?' — the words kept rushing through his mind. Then suddenly they stopped. 'Go *in*,' said a voice inside him. He walked slowly towards the gates and through the playground, then suddenly he heard somebody shout. He made up his mind. That shout was all he needed. 'RUN'. He turned and ran through the playground and then the gates. He dashed over the road and through the flats. All the time the voices said 'run, run' and he kept going. Outside a park about a mile away he stopped and thought. What had he done? He had been in the school, he had nearly made it. What had made him run? Why did he do it? David went into the park and sat down on one of the benches. There were so many questions but not enough answers.

He did not know how long he had sat in the park. Perhaps it was three hours, perhaps it was four. All he knew was that when he grew hungry he bought some chips and moved on to another park. Until at four o'clock that afternoon he plucked up the courage to go home. His parents did not say much as they half expected David to play truant. So did Mr Reed. He had phoned up and said that somebody should bring David in on Monday and then he could talk to Lawrence Dane, the school psychotherapist. David's mother would be taking David on Monday.

As much as he hated the idea, he would be going.

CHAPTER 12

PSYCHOTHERAPIST

Monday morning came. David got up and got ready for school. And for the second time in less than five days he set out for Selton, only this time with his mother. And as he got nearer and nearer, he again had to listen to the two sides of him battling it out. But today it would be different, because today he was going to force himself into the school. He knew he could quite easily get away from his mother. But no, he was going in. He had to make an effort.

He walked slowly through the gates and into the playground. David always thought it strange that whenever he was nervous or worried he seemed to grow very tired and weak. He did not have enough energy to do anything. He just wanted to go home and sleep. And on that cloudy Monday morning as he walked up the stairs of Selton Maladjusted School, going home and sleeping was definitely the only thing he wanted to do. They stopped outside the register room. 'Right', said Mrs Cook, 'go on, go in and I'll see you at lunch time. Okay?'

She turned and walked towards the stairs. David stood there and looked through the window of the classroom door. Mr Reed was sitting behind a table just in front of the blackboard and facing the class. He was 'trying' to call the register. David looked at the school. (All the classes joined together for the register taking). He looked at the three youths rolling up bits of plasticine and throwing them at other people. He looked at the boy kicking the back of the little girl's chair, and at the little girl crying. He saw the familiar face of Geoff sitting talking to another boy. Then he looked back at the class and shuddered. Should he go in or should he run away?

'Hi', said a voice behind him. He looked round and saw a young man with a beard and long hair and spectacles, smiling at him.

'You must be David Cook', he said in a faint Canadian accent.

'Yes', answered the surprised David.

'I'm Lawrence Dane, the school psychotherapist. I've been standing here for quite a while. You were wondering whether to go in or not, weren't you?'

David looked back at the class.

'Yes I was', he answered slowly.

'Why?' asked Mr Dane.

'I don't know, I just can't seem to go in'.

'Why, what's so bad about it?'

David shrugged his shoulders. 'I don't really know', he answered.

Mr Dane looked at him for a few seconds. 'Com'on', he said, 'let's go in, shall we?'

He opened the door and David walked in behind him. Everyone looked at him. Someone laughed. And David blushed slightly. He had never felt so frightened in all his life. He wished they would stop looking at him.

'Hello David', said Mr Reed. 'Come and sit down'.

David walked over to Geoff, all the time the children watched him. He sat down in the chair next to Geoff. Mr Dane sat next to Mr Hamilton.

'So you finally made it, I see', smiled Geoff.

'Yes', answered David.

Geoff introduced Ian to David. David sat there listening for his name to be called out. The assembly lasted for about fifteen minutes. Afterwards Mr Hamilton had said a few words about children coming in late. Mr Reed dismissed the school and everyone filed out of the room except for eight children, including Geoff and Ian. Mr Reed was going to teach them history. Mr Dane asked David to go to his room. It was the room next to Dr Garish's.

Mr Dane unlocked the door and David walked in. It was a very big room. Over in the corner was a piano and, scattered around it were lots of jigsaws and children's games. Over by the window was a large desk with two armchairs. The desk top was also full of games. On the wall next to the desk was a full-length mirror. And on the wall next to the door was a huge blackboard. David liked this room, it seemed very peaceful and quiet, unlike the rest of the school.

Mr Dane sat down on the armchair in front of the mirror and David sat on the other one.

'Well David, how about telling me a bit about yourself?' asked Mr Dane.

'Where shall I start?'

'Anywhere. Tell me all about your family'.

'Alright', said David. 'Well, first of all there's six of us. My dad and mum, my two brothers — Paul, he's eighteen, and then there's Stephen, he's fifteen; then there's me, I'm fourteen, and my little sister Hilary, she's seven'.

'I see', said Mr Dane.

David continued. 'My dad's a manager of a suede workshop. My mum's a phlebotomist. Paul works in a warehouse, and Stephen's still at school, so is Hilary and I'm', he paused, 'well,

I'm making a mess of everything'.

Why do you say that?' asked Mr Dane.

'Because I am. I haven't been to school regularly since I was at my primary school and that was three years ago. And I keep running away from every school I go to'.

'Why?'

'I don't know', said David quietly.

'Well, tell me what makes you run. What's it like standing outside the gates'.

'Well, I reach the gates and suddenly I just get so scared I have to run away. I just can't face the thought of school.'

'Why, what's so terrible about it?' asked Mr Dane.

'That's what I keep asking myself. I know nothing's going to happen to me, but every time I'm in a school I just have to get out. I feel as if I'm trapped'.

'Do you feel as if you're trapped now?'

'No, not really'.

'But you're in school'.

'I know, but for some reason I feel okay'.

'Would you feel okay if you were in one of the classes; say Mr Reed's?'

'I don't know. I might do, or I might not.'

'Well, let's give it a try, shall we?'

David hesitated. 'I'm not sure', he said. His heart suddenly started racing.

'Well, you don't know until you've tried, do you?' said Mr Dane.

'I suppose not', replied David slowly. He really did not want to go in, he did not like the look of any of the children. 'They might be a load of violent maniacs or something — you don't know with maladjusted kids', he thought. And he did not like the idea of the door being locked. Geoff had told him about that. 'But', he thought, 'I don't know till I try. It might be all right, who knows?'

He looked at Mr Dane, 'I'll give it a try', he said.

Mr Dane smiled. 'Well, Mr Reed's taking history at the moment, let's try him'. They got up and walked out of the room. Mr Dane locked the door. David followed Mr Dane along the hall to the register room. He knocked on the door and they walked in. David noticed the door was not locked. He felt a bit better. He immediately saw the smiling face of Geoff sitting next to Ian at a table in a corner. David expected it to be very noisy. But no, there were a few people talking, but they were not rushing around like maniacs, as he expected. And the atmosphere was quite friendly.

'David here said he would like to come in here and see how things are run', said Mr Dane.

'That's all right', smiled Mr Reed. He looked round the room. 'You know Geoff, don't you?' he asked. David nodded. 'Alright then go and sit next to him'.

David pulled a chair over to the table and sat on it between Geoff and Ian. There were only six other children in the room. They were sitting at a long table in the front of the class.

'Well', asked Geoff, 'What do you think of the school?'

'It's not bad', said David, 'it's not as mad as I thought it was going to be. I expected a load of screaming kids hanging from the chandelier'.

'That's what I expected as well', said Ian.

Mr Dane spoke to Mr Reed for a few minutes, then left. An hour later David was smiling for the first time since he had gone in to the school. He, Geoff and Ian were laughing at a joke that Mr Reed had told them. All he seemed to do all the lesson was tell jokes. This way he taught the children without their realising it.

When it was time for break, David and Geoff and Ian left the class and went out to the playground. They went over to the bench and sat down. David was feeling much better and he sat listening to Geoff's feeble jokes. Geoff told David about the annual school outing to the seaside that the school was going on in a few weeks.

Mr Dane came out and walked over to the boys. 'Well', he said to David, 'how was it?'

'Pretty good, it wasn't a bit like I thought it would be. I quite liked it'.

'That's great' smiled Mr Dane.

David looked round the playground. 'Yes it is', he said.

Mr Dane turned and walked back into the school again. David thought — it was 'great' this morning, but would it be tomorrow?

CHAPTER 13

WANDERERS RETURN

The next day David did manage to go into Selton. In fact he went in the next day too, and the next. And from then on he went in fairly regularly. Some mornings he would find it too hard to go in. But it seemed that David was finally beating his fear. He had overcome it so much in fact that he even agreed to go on the school's annual outing to the seaside. At any other school or time he would have probably refused to go. But with great will power and a lot of help from Mr Dane, David found himself sitting on the coach next to Geoff waiting for Mr Reed to finish calling the register.

It was a fine Thursday morning in the middle of September. And the weather looked very promising. There were four teachers on each of the two coaches. Mr Reed and Mr Hamilton along with the woodwork teacher and Mr Watts sat in the other coach with Mr Hamilton's class, and the children that Mr Reed taught history. David, Geoff and Ian should have been in the coach, but there was not enough room, so they were made to sit with the smaller children on the other coach.

Mr Reed checked the last name, and jumped down from the coach and closed the door. Everyone watched as he got onto the other coach, said something to the driver, and the coach pulled out into the road.

'We're off,' smiled Geoff.

It was Ian who, sitting in the seat behind David and Geoff, started singing. He was soon joined by David and Geoff and a few of the other children. At first they were singing some well-chosen songs from the pages of a rugby song book. But they soon got round to the top twenty of that time.

The two coaches sped on through the country-side heading for their destination, with the children shouting through the windows at innocent passersby. Until a policecar stopped next to them at the traffic lights, then they were all quiet.

It was two hours later after finally getting out of a traffic jam that the coaches pulled up in the coach park opposite the pier. Mrs Buckley jumped up and blocked the doorway.

'Now,' she said, 'make sure you get back here by a quarter to three or we go without you. And make sure you don't get into any trouble.'

After everyone had received the packed lunches, Mr Reed said the older children could go their own way. But they were to make sure they were back in time. There was a fun-fair about two miles away from the pier. So David, Geoff, Ian and a few others decided to head for that. They waited on the other side of the road for a bus which came and they got on and sat upstairs. David, Geoff and Ian were the only ones to get on the bus as the others had decided to walk.

'We've got to go easy on our money,' said David, checking his pockets.

'I'm all right,' remarked Ian proudly, displaying two pound notes.

'That's twice as much as I've got,' exclaimed Geoff, not liking the thought of Ian having more money than himself.

'I've got to get some sticks of rock and sweets with this,' said Ian, holding one of the pound notes.

A few minutes later the bus reached the town centre and the fun-fair. The boys got off the bus and stood outside the fun-fair and a chip shop, debating whether to go into the fun-fair before buying chips, or vice-versa. But they soon made up their minds. The haunted house caught their eye and the attraction of it was more overpowering than the chip shop, and they were drawn towards it like a magnet.

It was five pence admission. They paid and walked along a narrow cat-walk and into a dark corridor. The corridor was about three feet wide and ultra-violet lights shone down on the boys making their black clothes shine white and the white clothes black. They looked like negatives of a photograph. They walked round a corner.

'Bloody hell!' shouted the silhouetted figure of Geoff. 'I can't stand up! The floor's moving!'

Ian was the next victim of the moving floor. Suddenly there was a thud and David, who was also trying to move on, could do nothing but laugh at the sight of Geoff crawling around on the floor, trying to stand up.

'Jesus Christ!' he shouted. 'This bloody floor's bashing my knees in. Help me up will yer!'

The laughing Ian and David took hold of Geoff's arm and helped him up on to his feet and the three boys struggled off the rocking, swinging floor.

The next corridor was full of bits of hanging string that were meant to frighten people, and luminous pictures and models of rather pathetic-looking monsters. The scenery was accompanied by a tape recording of screaming high-pitched noises.

They walked round another corner and were immediately faced by three weird-shaped creatures with four eyes. David burst out laughing.

'They're our reflections,' he shouted. 'They're mirrors.'

After a lot of face-pulling and shouting, the boys staggered out and headed for the 'super speed racing track' as it was called. It was a figure eight track and where the track crossed over, it went up into a small bridge. The small solidly built cars were not actually 'super speed' but they were fairly fast.

'Come on,' said David, 'let's go on these.'

'Alright,' said Geoff.

The boys paid their money and they were shown over to three rather shabby-looking cars. Ian, David and Geoff jumped in. David pushed the pedal down. At first the car started off slowly but it soon gathered speed, it reached about twenty m.p.h., which was about the maximum. David and Ian were soon whizzing round the track. But Geoff, who had got in a car last, was just lurching forward and shifting his weight trying to get the car to move. One of the attendants, a young man, came rushing over to him.

'What's the trouble?' he asked.

'I can't get the car to move,' answered Geoff.

The man went to the back of the car and got into a position to push it. 'Right,' he shouted over the noise of the other cars, 'have you got your foot on the pedal?'

'What pedal?' enquired Geoff impatiently.

'Bloody hell!' cried the attendant, 'how do you expect it to move if you don't push the pedal?'

'Well, I didn't know, did I?' said Geoff defensively.

The man had got off the track just in time to get out of the way as David went smashing into the back of Geoff's car.

'Blimey!' said David, as his machine bounced off the back of Geoff's and into some unused cars. Geoff who was unharmed as his brakes were on when David hit him, laughed and pushed down on the pedal. David just sat there trembling and nursing his injured shin that he had knocked when he hit the back of Geoff's car. The attendant again came running over. David waited for the expected words of sympathy like 'are you okay?' but his illusion was soon shattered by the man's voice.

'For Christ's sake watch where you're going, will yer?'

The man pulled David's car out from the middle of the unused ones. David pushed down on the pedal again and swung around the bend the same time as Geoff, who took one hand off the steering wheel and made rude signs at his friend. With one hand off the wheel he lost all control of the car and hit the corner at fifteen m.p.h. Again the attendant came running over and again he had to leap out of the way as Ian swung round the corner towards him. The man got Geoff mobile again and for once all three boys were actually driving around the track at the same time. They went round four times without any injuries until David went too wide turning a corner and he crashed into the same group of unused cars as before. But this time Ian was so close behind him that there was not enough room to move and he went into the back of David. Geoff was the next to come round the corner. And because Ian had bounced off David's car he was now in the car's path. There was a loud crunch and Geoff came to a halt.

The three stunned boys sat in the equally stunned cars and looked at each other. As it was the middle of the week and the month of September, there was nobody else on the track to be involved in the accident. For about the tenth time in less than ten minutes the attendant of the 'Super Speed Racing Track' came over to David Cook, Geoffrey Moller and Ian Goodman.

'Right, that's yer lot,' he said looking as if he were about to explode at any moment.

'But can't we go a little bit longer?' asked Geoff.

'You've got to be kidding! You've only been here a few minutes and look at the damage you've done in that time!'

The boys looked down at the cars. 'Yeah, you're right,' said David. He looked at the other two. 'Come on' he said, 'let's go.'

They limped slowly away watched by the attendant to make sure they didn't break anything else.

'I never want to go on there again,' said David examining the graze on his shin.

'Me neither,' remarked Ian.

'I don't know,' said Geoff, 'I thought it was pretty good.' David looked at him.

'Yeah, you would do, you masochist.'

Geoff ignored the insult. He pointed to the aeroplanes (hissing air pumps made them move).

'Let's go on there,' he said.

Opposite them was an arcade. Inside were hot dog stalls and souvenir shops and a penny arcade, and various other stalls. The boys passed under a dome and into the arcade which was a long type of tunnel. To reach the aeroplanes the boys had to go through the arcade. On either side, the stall holders were trying frantically to attract the boys' attention to try their luck at darts, or get the balls into the holes, and things like that. But the boys just shrugged these attractions aside by shaking their heads and walking on. As there was no-one around, customers were like gold and were treated as such. The boys were definitely enjoying themselves.

They reached the aeroplanes and paid their money. There were four planes altogether and they were supposed to look like world war fighting planes. They had two doors; David climbed in one and Geoff in the other. As there was no more room, Ian had to go on his own in another machine. The boys strapped themselves in and took hold of the two joy sticks in front of them. David made a joke about being afraid of heights and the planes started moving around. David's side of the plane was slanting down at an angle of 30 degrees, so the boys decided to straighten the plane up.

'But we don't know how to control it,' shouted David.

'So what,' said Geoff, 'let's try turning this way.'

David and Geoff turned the joysticks outward, the plane turned and the boys found themselves looking up at the ground. 'Get it straight!' shouted David. 'Get it straight!' They turned the joysticks inwards and again the inside wing was sloping downwards at a thirty degree angle. The boys managed to keep the plane like that until the end of the ride. But Ian was not so lucky. The plane was very heavy — too heavy for one person to control. Throughout the ride David and Geoff watched Ian's plane go round and round. The ride finally stopped. The two dizzy boys jumped down from the plane and staggered over to Ian. They started laughing at the green-faced Ian sitting there repeating the words 'I feel sick' over and over again. They helped him out and went to find a more peaceful amusement.

They noticed a sign saying 'Mystic caves,' and headed in that direction. The 'mystic caves' turned out to be something like the tunnel of love, but because Ian was not fit enough to go on anything else, they decided to go in. They paid and got into a boat and were pushed into the beginning of the cave. There were several small wheels below the water that caused a current strong enough to push the boats all round the tunnels.

The walls of the cave were brightly covered with pictures of Aladin and Sinbad and other such heroes of fairy tales. The tunnel was lined with soft lights.

'I feel a right burk,' said Geoff. 'I mean in a tunnel like this I should be with a bird. Not you two idiots.'

'Thanks very much,' replied David, 'you can't know how lucky you are to be able to talk to a genius like me,' he laughed.

After they had been through the tunnel, the boys thought they would like to go on the Helter-Skelter, which was round the back of the Haunted House. The boys paid their money and walked up a long staircase to the top. The Helter-Skelter was of a special kind. The slide was not on the outside, but on the inside and at the bottom was a type of big bowl that was designed so that people could slide round the top of it a few times then slowly slide to the middle of the bowl.

David, Geoff and Ian picked up three of the carpets from a pile next to the beginning of the slide. Ian went first and David and Geoff saw him disappear round the first bend. Geoff was the next to go, followed by David. There were four bends altogether. The boys gathered speed very quickly. Geoff and Ian had been on this kind of Helter-Skelter before so they knew what to expect. But David had not. And suddenly the wall on the right of him seemed to disappear. He thought it was the end of the world. But the wall had not disappeared, he had just reached the bowl. He had only been that frightened once before and that was when he had started at Selton.

Everyone picked themselves up and put their carpets on the pile as they made their way out of the Helter-Skelter. The day wore on. The boys went on everything in the fun-fair until David looked at his watch. (He was the only one that had a watch).

'We'd better be making our way back to the coach. It's quarter past two'.

David, Ian and Geoff made their way out of the fun-fair and over to the bus stop. They reached the bus stop opposite the coach park. There were two entrances to the coach park and the inside could not be seen from the bus stop as a tall hedge ran the length of it. The three boys crossed the road and went through the entrance directly opposite them. The other entrance was a couple of hundred yards away down the road. The coaches were right next to the other entrance.

'It's all right', said Geoff, 'we're not late'.

Just then the two coaches started up and drove out of the other entrance. David's watch was a half hour slow. 'Run', shouted David. They all started running but stopped when they realised they would not catch the coaches.

'Now what are we going to do?' said the exhausted Ian.

'Well, we're going to have to go by train', said Geoff.

David turned to his friend. 'But we haven't got any money. We spent it all in the fun-fair'.

Geoff grinned. 'Have no fear, Geoff is here', he said proudly. 'All we have to do is get a train to Upminster, change over to the District line and when we get there, say we came from the next station up and pay three pence. Brilliant!'

David looked at Geoff is disgust. 'But that's dishonest', he said.

'I know it is you idiot, but how else are we going to get home?'

'But supposing we get caught?'

'Look, don't worry. It'll be all right. All we have to do is go straight past the ticket office and there we are. And anyway, I don't know why you're complaining, we should be having a go at you. If your bleeding watch hadn't gone wrong, we wouldn't have missed the coaches in the first place'.

David realised that he was not going to win. 'Alright', he said, 'let's find the station'.

The first part of Geoff's plan worked smoothly. Nobody stopped them as they went through the station and out to the platform. As it turned out, the whole plan went well. They reached home without any trouble and the ticket collector believed their story. It was six o'clock by then and they all decided to go to David's house and tell his parents what had happened. Mrs Cook told them that they had to go back to the school and tell the headmaster, as he would probably be very worried. They all walked back to Selton where the caretaker told them that the coaches had not arrived back yet.

'Right then', said David, 'we'll wait'.

They waited for over an hour but there was still no sign of the coaches. So the boys went home.

David was woken the next morning by the high-pitched voice of his little sister saying, 'You're on the radio, you're on the radio!'

David jumped out of bed and rushed up to the kitchen where his mother told him that the news reader said that seven children had gone missing the day before on an outing. It was a London school called Selton.

'Seven', thought David, 'there were only three of us!'

He took it that as usual the reports had been exaggerated. But they had not. As it turned out, seven children *had* gone missing. Geoff, David and Ian by accident and four others. They had planned it as they thought it would cause a stir (as it did) and be a 'laugh'.

Mr Reed did not think it was a 'laugh'; in fact he took it very seriously indeed. Naturally he thought that David, Ian and Geoff were with the others and had 'arranged' not to come back. But he believed their story and realised that they had not been with the others. After a light telling off, he let them go.

'You know what?' said Geoff as they made their way to the art room, 'we were lucky to get off that lightly. I mean, he could have really had a go if he wanted to'.

'Yeah, I suppose you're right', said David. 'Anyway, let's forget it now shall we?'

The two boys nodded and David opened the door of the art room.

CHAPTER 14

CAUGHT IN THE ACT

It was four weeks since that day at the fun-fair and everyone was at assembly. Mr Reed had called out the register, and Mrs Buckley went up to the front of the class, 'I'm thinking of starting a photography class', she said, 'so if anyone would like to be included in it, just give your names to me and, after assembly we'll go straight up to the dark room next to John's (Mr Reed) room okay?'

Nearly all the school wanted to be in the photography class, Geoff, Ian, David and Teresa Doves were the first people to be picked for the class, and they were taken up to the dark room after assembly. Mrs Buckley unlocked the door, walked in and turned on the light. The room was crammed with old model cars. It looked more like a toy shop than a dark room. A large developer stood on top of a table next to three trays. Mrs Buckley showed the boys and Teresa how it worked. She took a camera off the shelf.

'I've already taken some photos', she said. 'Now the light has got to be turned out before I can take the film out, then we've got to put the film in here'. She pointed to a small drum and took off the lid.

'Turn off the light', she said. Teresa turned off the light and Mrs Buckley started fumbling around with the camera. Geoff, who was standing next to Teresa, felt something was climbing up the inside of his leg. He reached down and found he was holding Teresa's hand. He turned around and his body pressed against hers and they started kissing. It was very dark so they could not be seen.

'Now', said Mrs Buckley, 'I've put the film into the drum'. She put the lid tightly down.

'Okay', she said, 'put the light on'.

Geoff had his clothes adjusted and was on the other side of the room by the time the light was switched on. Everybody squinted in the sudden brightness.

'I've got to take this to the staff room' said Mrs Buckley, holding up the drum. Teresa stared at Geoff.

'This has got to be soaked in water for about half an hour', said Mrs Buckley. She gave them a negative of a photograph. 'Now you know how it works', she said, pointing to the big machine on the table. 'If you get into any trouble, just come to the staff room'. She went out of the room and shut the door.

'Has she left the keys?' asked Geoff.

'No', answered David.

'Never mind', said Geoff, looking at Teresa, 'we'll just have to keep our ears open then', he winked at her. Teresa smiled. She slowly unbuttoned her dress and it dropped silently to the floor. She unclipped her bra and that too dropped to the floor. Geoff moved towards her. Suddenly they heard footsteps outside the door. Everyone froze.

'Quick Teresa', said Geoff, 'you get dressed and we'll try stopping whoever it is from coming in here'.

Teresa nodded and proceeded to get dressed. The three boys quickly opened the door, went out and shut it. The footsteps were the headmaster's. He looked at Geoff.

'I was just coming to see who was in the dark room' he said.

'We're in there', replied Geoff feverishly. The three of them had arranged themselves into a human wall. Geoff in front of Mr Reed, David just behind him and Ian standing holding the door closed. Mr Reed noticed the strange looks on the boys' faces, he did not realise it was shock.

'Is something wrong, Geoff?' he asked.

'N-no, nothing at all', hesitated Geoff. What was he going to do? He would just have to stop Mr Reed going into the dark room and seeing Teresa getting dressed. He just had to keep talking. 'It's a good idea of Mrs Buckley having a photography class, isn't it Sir?' he said.

'Yes it is'.

'We're not doing too bad'.

'Well that's good', said Mr Reed. 'I think I'll go in and see for myself. I like a bit of photography'. He moved to go past Geoff.

'You can't go in there Sir', cried Geoff.

Mr Reed looked even more puzzled.

'No, you definitely can't go in', agreed David.

'Why on earth not?' asked the headmaster.

'Because', said Geoff, searching for an answer, 'because we're in the middle of developing. And if you open the door, you'll ruin the photo'.

'You will, Sir', supported David.

'But you're not developing are you? You're out here talking to me. Oh, by the way, it's break. I thought you might like to know'.

He moved Geoff aside and opened the door.

The three boys had never run so fast in their lives! They ran down the stairs, into the playground and out of the school. They ran across the road, around the corner and stopped outside a block of flats. Puffing and wheezing they leant up against the wall.

'Jesus Christ', said David, 'what are we going to do *now?*

We're in *real* trouble'. He pictured what had happened when Mr Reed saw Teresa getting dressed. 'What are we going to do?'he repeated.

'Look', said Geoff, 'we'll go for a walk and have a cup of tea and we'll all figure out what to do, okay?' David and Ian nodded. The three boys walked down to Whitehill Market and went into a cafe and sat down at one of the tables with a cup of tea each.

'Now', said Geoff, 'if we say that we were larking about and Teresa started doing a strip, and we say we didn't do anything, then we'll be all right'.

'Don't be stupid', said David, 'you don't think Father John's going to believe that do you?'

Geoff thought. 'No, I suppose not', he said slowly.

They talked for about an hour until David came up with the best idea. 'Look', he said, 'we don't know what happened, do we? Maybe she got dressed in time. So I reckon we should go back and face the music'.

They all agreed and walked slowly back to the school. The first person they saw as they walked through the gates was Teresa. she came bouncing over to them with a broad smile on her face.

'Well?' asked Geoff, 'what happened?'

'Nothing', answered Teresa.

The boys looked surprised. 'Nothing?' enquired Geoff. 'What do you mean?'

'Well', she went on, 'I managed to get dressed and when the old man came in all he said was, it was a good photo'.

The boys looked at her in disbelief. 'Are you sure?' asked David. 'He didn't say anything else?'

'Of course I'm sure'.

Just then Mr Reed came down the stairs. He saw the boys and came over to them.

'Here we go', said Geoff under his breath.

'I saw that photo of the Tower and I thought it was very good, excellent'. He patted David on the back and walked away in the direction of the gymnasium. The three boys watched him in amazement.

'He didn't kill us', said David.

'Nothing at all', said Ian.

'Not even a dirty look', said Geoff.

The boys decided to wipe away the memory of the afternoon altogether, so they went up to the drama class. Mrs Buckley and Mr Dane were in charge of the class. About twelve children, including David, Ian and Geoff were in it. All three boys liked the drama class very much. They could do whatever they wanted.

They were the only people including Teresa that actually perform-ed anything; the others just charged about shouting and yelling. Occasionally a group of the smaller boys would do something, but it always ended the same way with a pitched battle between the cowboys and indians, or superman and his arch enemies, the British troops against the Germans or something like that.

David and Geoff took it very seriously. Geoff saw himself as a budding script writer (as he wrote most of the material for the drama class) and a Lawrence Olivier and an all-round genius. David did not have such big ambitions; he just saw himself as a Lawrence Olivier, and of course a genius.

They opened the door of Mr Dane's room and walked in. They were immediately greeted by Mrs Buckley's smiling face.

'Just the people I wanted to see', she said.

'Why?' asked Geoff.

'Well', she said, 'I know Christmas is still a good three months away, but as you three are the best performers we've had in this school, I decided that we're going to do a show for Christmas'.

Geoff smiled, 'Well, you came to the right person – me'. He gazed at his fingernails. 'I suppose', he said, 'that you want me to write a few things?'

'Well of course. You're the best person we've got', smiled Mrs Buckley.

'I couldn't agree more', said Geoff proudly.

'Big head', said Mrs Buckley.

CHAPTER 15

BATTLE MATCH

The football season had started.

'We'll kill 'em', said little Stephen Crossman, one of the players of the school's football team. It was assembly and the team were playing a vital match that afternoon. Stephen swung his kit-bag over his shoulder.

Selton's first match of the season was against Bridgeway, a tough opposition from South London that had finished something like sixth in the league the previous season. Mr Hamilton had heard about Stephen's prophesy on the game.

'Don't be too sure', he shouted from the other side of the room, 'we finished up eighth in the league last season remember'.

'That's not bad going', commented Stephen.

'But there're only nine teams in the league', remarked Mr Hamilton.

'Oh', said Stephen, 'so there are'.

The league consisted of eight other maladjusted schools from different parts of London. So far, nobody had been able to topple Renfield, (a tough team also from South London) off the top of the league, for something like four seasons. Mr Reed hushed the conversation and sat down on a chair in front of the table and started calling out the names. 'Well, well, well', he said, glancing round the room, 'isn't it strange, as soon as the football season begins the little faces start to appear again'. He grinned.

After assembly, Mr Hamilton came to the front of the class and arranged the football team. He picked up a piece of chalk and and drew a diagram of the positions that the team would be in— on the blackboard.

At 12.45 the coach pulled up outside the school to take the team to the place where the match would be played. There was still half an hour left of break, so Geoff and Ian decided to visit the park that the girls from the nearby school used when they took sandwiches for lunch. David could still not manage to go to school for two weeks without playing truant, perhaps it was habit – he wasn't sure, but this was one of his 'off' days.

Geoff noticed two nice looking girls sitting on the grass in the park. Geoff and Ian went over to them and sat down. The girls were about five yards away. They were aware of the boys. The boys, knowing this, started trying to break into conversation with them.

'The price of toilet paper today, it's quite ridiculous', grinned

Geoff. The girls giggled. One of them threw a crisp which floated in the air and landed next to Geoff. He picked it up and looked at it in mock disgust. He walked over to the girls still holding the crisp. 'Did you know', he said, 'that it is an offence to drop litter?' The three girls giggled and looked at each other.

'Do you go to that mental school round the corner?' one of them asked.

'Do you mean Selton?' asked Geoff.

'Yeah, that's the one. Selton'.

'It's not a 'mental' school', said Geoff, almost spitting the words, 'it's a school for maladjusted kids'.

'Oh', said the girl slightly embarrassed.

'I bet you don't know what a maladjusted school is', he went on with real feeling for the school in his voice.

'No, not really', said the girl, 'but I know it's for mad kids'.

Geoff looked at her in disgust. 'No', he said, 'I didn't think you'd know'. If there was one type of person he could not tolerate (Ian also) it was one such as this girl. She was someone who was ready to kick another person when he was down. She did not even know the meaning of the word 'maladjusted', in fact she had never heard it before Geoff had told her, yet she would accuse anybody going to a maladjusted school as being 'mad' or 'mental'. Geoff didn't even understand the word. People like her just would not believe their eyes if they ever visited a school like Selton, for they would be very perplexed to find out that maladjusted children do not leap about the school attacking people. Although Geoff himself had been under the same impression when he had first joined the school, his views soon changed and he felt he was doing the right thing in defending Selton and schools like it. He had been to quite a few schools and never met teachers like those of Selton. In most other schools the teachers didn't have time for anything. A few teachers had been willing to help Geoff overcome his problem, but most of them could not be bothered. But in Selton it was different. Any teacher would help with a problem at any time, in school or out of it, especially the headmaster. If a former pupil was having a hard time finding a job then he would help him or her.

Geoff looked down at the girls. When he had first walked into the park he thought they were attractive, but as soon as the first girl had commented on Selton, Geoff was suddenly put off them. 'Come on', he said to Ian, 'let's go'.

Having got all the football team aboard the coach, Mr Hamilton told the driver to start. It was a little further to Bridgeway's ground then Selton's and it took the coach forty-five minutes to get there. Mr Hamilton started counting the players.

'What's happened to David? I thought he was coming along to watch?' he asked.

'I think he's gone out with the others to the zoo', answered Geoff, knowing full well that David was probably sitting in a park somewhere.

'Don't give me that', said Mr Hamilton, 'he's bunked off somewhere, hasn't he?'

Geoff and Ian nodded.

'Well at least we've got a few other spectators', said Mr Hamilton.

He turned and walked down to the front seat. The coach pulled up outside a small football pitch. The captain of the team, Billy Page, picked up the two footballs and started throwing them up in the air.

'All right', said Mr Hamilton, 'pack it up'.

As there were no changing rooms, the boys got changed on the coach, then got off and had to wait for about twenty minutes until the Bridgeway team pulled up. Geoff could not stand kicking the ball about, he would rather sit down and talk. When finally the Bridgeway team came 'About time', said Mr Hamilton, looking at his watch. The door of the coach slid open and the Bridgeway team filed out. Geoff thought they looked rather menacing. At least half the team were much bigger than Ian and and Geoff, and Ian was a good four inches taller than Geoff. A rather thin, spotty boy walked down the steps of the coach wearing a green football shirt and, strangely enough, a deerstalker, which made him look like Sherlock Holmes in a football kit. He also wore black leather gloves. He was obviously the goal-keeper.

The Bridgeway sports master walked over to Mr Hamilton and started talking to him. He then took his coat off, gave it to one of the Bridgeway spectators, and walked into the centre of the pitch. He gestured to the two sides to take up their positions. In a few minutes the game had started.

One of the Bridgeway team darted through the middle of Selton's defence. Tony, a well-built coloured boy ran over to intercept the ball which was over the heads of the Selton attackers. With a mighty kick he sent the ball whizzing over to the Bridgeway half where Ian seized it. Four Bridgeway defenders who were built like buffaloes charged at him. Ian wisely passed it to Geoff out on the right wing.

Suddenly the whole Selton attack seemed to surge forward. Geoff now had the ball, he went round one defender then another. Ian was screaming at the top of his voice for the ball over by the Bridgeway goal. He soon found himself surrounded by the defenders.

Stephen was also near the goal; he held his head high as he waited for the ball. The ball came but he missed and struck his head on the post.

Then 'Sherlock Holmes' grasped the ball and kicked it down to the Selton end of the pitch where a Bridgeway striker was lurking dangerously near the goal. Frantically Selton defenders rushed towards him; with a neat 'dummy' he ran round the two defenders and sent the ball whizzing into the back of the Selton goal — 1 - 0 to Bridgeway. Later on in the first half Bridgeway scored again to make it 2 - 0. Things were looking bad for Selton as they sat on their bench at half time.

After a pre-second half talk from Mr Hamilton, Selton walked slowly back on to the pitch. Suddenly Selton scored a goal; Geoff Moller crossed from the right wing and the goal was scored by a spectacular diving header by Ian to bring them to two-one to Bridgeway. Geoff had decided to stay next to the Bridgeway goal hoping for a quick break. It did not come until late in the second half. Stephen Crossman went rushing through the middle of the field with the ball at his feet. He looked up and saw Geoff darting in front of the goalkeeper. Stephen kicked the ball and it went flying into the goal. It was now two-two. The goalkeeper gave Geoff a sneer; Geoff being in front of him had put him off. From now on Geoff and the goalkeeper would not be the best of friends.

There were about twenty minutes left to play when the ball went whizzing across the field to Geoff. He pounced on it and ran with it towards the Bridgeway goal. There was only the goalkeeper stopping Geoff from scoring the goal. The goalkeeper ran out to try and block Geoff's shot but he knew the only way he could stop Geoff now was to foul him. Ian was screaming for the ball over by the far post. The goalkeeper flew out to Geoff, only to see the ball shoot over to Ian who had no difficulty in tapping home yet another goal. All the Bridgeway team bellowed at the sports teacher for an offside decision. But their master said no, it was a goal. The team started to lose their tempers. John ran towards the ball to tackle a Bridgeway player. The player pulled out a knife.

'If you want the ball come and get it', he shouted. Everyone watched as John stepped back. His boot shot out towards the boy's wrist; there was a 'crack' and the knife dropped to the ground. Another Bridgeway player rushed over to John and punched him in the mouth. Again John's boot came up, this time the boy fell to the ground clutching his groin and screaming. Suddenly another Bridgeway player came from behind John and jumped him. They fell to the ground kicking and punching.

The boy that had had the knife went to try and kick John whilst he was on the ground. But one of the Selton players saw this and he ran over and jumped on the boy. Suddenly the whole field seemed to erupt into one bloody battle. Kicks and punches were everywhere. Mr Hamilton, the bus driver and the Bridgeway teacher rushed over to stop the battle which was now at its height. A fist smashed against a Bridgeway player's face, his nose burst open and blood came gushing out. He stood there screaming with his hands over his bloody face. Geoff watched all this from the end of the pitch. The three men managed to break the fighting up. Mr Hamilton pulled John out of the crowd of fighting boys. His nose was bleeding badly.

'What happened?' asked Mr Hamilton.

'I went to get the ball and the bastard pulled a knife out on me', answered John. 'He's a bloody nutter'.

A boy of about fifteen years lay trembling on the ground holding his groin. He was picked up but could not stand. His legs were like jelly and for the rest of the match he had to sit down.

Selton won four-two after Ian made a beautiful solo effort beating three men and the goalkeeper to put the ball in the net. The match finished and Selton were made to drink up the orange juice (it was always supplied by the home team) very quickly. The atmosphere on the Selton coach was far from quiet as the team talked about 'their first great win' and the fight and the goalkeeper's funny hat that blew off his head every time he bent down.

Mr Hamilton was a little more quiet. He congratulated the team on winning the match. But as for the fighting, well, the boys had to make sure that did not happen again. He could say no more as he wasn't very sure what had happened.

CHAPTER 16

BEAUTY QUEEN OF SELTON

A strange thing occurred the following Monday. Mr Reed and Mr Hamilton had been hearing about how many times the older boys had been taking advantage of Teresa Doves, so the headmaster decided to find out more. After assembly all the older boys, including David, Geoff and Ian, were made to go to Dr Garish's room where Mr Hamilton and Mr Reed could have a frank talk with them. The boys went into the room (about twelve of them) and waited until Mr Reed came in. He locked the door and sat down.

Mr Reed sat beside Mr Hamilton on a chair at the desk. Geoff, Ian and David sat on the carpet along with the other nine or so boys. Now and again a small child would look through the window of the door to see what was happening. Mr Reed would wave them away to their classroom. Mr Hamilton fiddled with the circular dialling discs on the telephone as the headmaster began to speak.

'Now then', he said, looking at the boys, 'I've heard a lot of talk about Teresa Doves', he paused, 'and you boys. Now we're going to have a frank and truthful talk', he glanced at Mr Hamilton and then to Geoff, Ian and David. 'Now you three, supposing you tell me your side of the story. The truth'.

The three boys knew that it was best to tell the truth, after all Mr Hamilton and Mr Reed would understand.

'Well sir', Geoff began, 'I don't think that she's been with anybody else. I think the only boys she's been with is me, David and Ian'.

Mr Reed nodded. Now he would find out if all the stories *were* true; he suspected the majority of them were not.

'The first time I went with her', Geoff said, 'was just after school. Me, Ian and Dave were walking along Cartridge Street when we saw her coming towards us. I don't know where she'd been, anyway, we saw her coming towards us and we went up to her and started talking, probably because we'd heard that she was supposed to have fancied all three of us'.

Someone in the room laughed for a second in disbelief. Geoff ignored it. 'So we started talking to her and we noticed that all the time she kept on talking about well, er sex, so we took this as an invitation and before we knew where we were, me, Ian and David were round my house. My mum and dad were at work and we were on the couch with her'.

Ian nodded as if to confirm the story. David sat saying nothing. 'Very interesting', said Mr Reed, 'tell me more'.

'Well sir', said Ian, 'after that she must have thought that we were madly in love with her for some reason' — again the laughter — 'because we went with her a second time'.

David spoke. 'You know that day when you came up to the darkroom and we wouldn't let you in?' Mr Reed nodded. 'Well, we weren't developing photos'.

The headmaster smiled, 'I did know, I'm not as stupid as I looked, but I thought that as I'd put you to so much misery, I wouldn't say anything'.

Geoff looked at the headmaster. 'So he did know!' he thought, 'he doesn't miss anything'. That was the good thing about a maladjusted school. All the teachers were so much friendlier. Take the headmaster for instance, he could have caused a lot of trouble for the three boys but he did not, as he understood the problem. And, as there are not many children there is a much better relationship between child and teacher. And also the teachers from Selton would talk freely about their home life and about their families, unlike other teachers. Even getting to know their first names would be remarkable! And the one thing Geoff liked was that the teachers in Selton would never call anyone by their surnames as in other schools. This gave a feeling of warm friendship between teacher and child. Geoff also liked this. In other schools when a teacher said 'Moller, come here', it made him feel very unimportant.

The talk in the small room lasted for about an hour with David, Geoff and Ian telling their story. Mr Reed's voice changed to a more serious tone. 'Now', he said, 'I realise that really all the rumours about Teresa Doves are not true, except for David, Ian's and Geoff's. But from now on when any of you get the 'urge', please stay away from Teresa — especially you three'. He looked at David, Ian and Geoff. 'If you don't watch yourselves, you'll end up doing something silly, and before you know where you are, you'll be in a lot of trouble, and you'll be sorry. Now is that understood?' The boys nodded. The headmaster was right.

The discussion ended after Mr Reed told everyone not to breathe a word about it to Teresa. The boys opened the door and went back to their classes. Geoff, Ian and David and a few others who were in the drama group (this also acted as a type of therapy class) stopped outside Mr Dane's room where Mr Dane was waiting for the rest of the group and for Mrs Buckley.

(David saw Mr Dane on Tuesday afternoons as well. Then they would talk over David's problems and this way he could overcome them. It had helped him a lot. Some days he could not get into school, but considering he had been running away from it for the past three and a half years, well that wasn't bad at all. He was actually experiencing something that he hadn't for the past three and a half years been able to. In other schools he would feel sick in the morning at the thought of attending. Now sometimes he would *look forward to school*. This pleased him very much. He no longer felt depressed).

Teresa Doves was also in the drama group and David noticed her as soon as he went into the room. She was sitting on a table fiddling about with some chalk. She smiled when she saw the three boys come into the room.

Christmas was now only about five weeks away so David and Geoff had already started organising things and writing out a script. They would have to start rehearsing if they were to be in time for Christmas. The drama class was spent deciding items for the show and keeping the other children quiet while doing so.

The four week gap between the day of the discussion and the show closed quickly. It was now only two weeks until the Christmas festivities. David went to school even more regularly for he was so engrossed with the show. By now the Christmas atmosphere began to show. Mrs Buckley asked David, Geoff and a few others to help her put up some decorations.

It was a cold December afternoon and David had just been home for lunch and was now making his way back to Selton to put up the last of the decorations. It was very misty and the morning frost had still not left the pavements of Little Turner Street. David shut the front door and pulled the hood up of his parka to help shield him against the cold. He turned into New - ton Road and then into Cartridge Street and toward the school. He was looking forward to the show and to the party he was going to and also his uncle's party he was going to, and to Christmas itself. He was feeling on top of the world. A year earlier he would have thought it impossible that he could feel so good walking toward any school gates. But that was history, it was all behind him now. With a lot of willpower and help from the teachers and Mr Dane he could actually enjoy himself in school. A year earlier he thought that his life was not worth living, he had forgotten what feeling happy was like. His whole life consisted of running away. But he could never get anywhere. Everywhere he went his fear went with him and he always felt depressed. He wondered if his fear would ever come back. He shook the terrible thought away and walked into the hall where Geoff was balancing on top of a twenty-foot ladder trying to put up a paper chain. Geoff was being assisted by Ian, Mrs Buckley and Stephen Crossman. The six-foot paper chain was too heavy for sellotape to hold and Geoff watched as it dropped from the ceiling and fell silently to the floor. He swore and came down the ladder to retrieve the chain. David laughed, 'Ever thought of getting a job with the people that put up the Oxford Street illuminations?' he shouted across the hall.

Geoff turned around, 'Oh', he said, 'I see you decided to come at last. You're twenty minutes late'.

'If you don't belt up', remarked David, 'I'll strangle you with that paper chain'. Geoff laughed, 'Look, take your coat off and help me do this', he said.

David took his coat off and went back into the hall. 'Why are there so many decorations anyway? You don't need all this lot', he said, handing Geoff some tinsel. 'Because', said Geoff, 'this is where we're having the school Christmas party. It's tomorrow'.

The party itself was a noisy affair with the usual music, dancing and food. There were jellies and cakes all over the floor and hoards of screaming children. Still it was a good party.

The school 'spectacular' was now only a week away. Mr Lamb the school caretaker erected the thick red curtains that had been in the storeroom and had not been used for years around the stage, and ringed them into place in the iron rails that hung down from the ceiling. Lighting was a little harder. Bulbs had to be arranged so that they shone down on to the stage. A red beam shone towards the back of the stage and a clear light shone directly on the front. The whole stage was chaos but things *were* getting done. They had hung the last curtain up after it had fallen down six times and David and Geoff had gone back to David's house after school as Geoff had left his bicycle lamp there.

David opened the front door and Geoff walked into the passage and shut the door behind him.

'It's in here', said David, pointing to the door of the bottom room. He opened the door and walked in. Geoff stood in the doorway with his mouth wide open with surprise. 'You've been burgled', he mumbled. The only furniture in the room was a table in the corner, five chairs against the wall by the window, the record player and two speakers. On the ceiling were decorations. David laughed at the surprised look on Geoff's face. 'Don't worry we haven't been burgled', he said, 'the furniture's in the other room. I had to clear the room because I'm having a party Saturday night for Christmas. I did this last night. I thought I would save some time if I did it a couple of days before'.

Geoff walked across the room and picked up his bicycle lamp from the mantlepiece. He looked round the room. 'Who's coming to this party? Me, I hope?'

'Of course', said David.

'Who else?'

'Michael, a few other boys and some girls; the ones from Judo. And George'.

'Does he have to come?'

'Well it is the season of peace and goodwill to all men. And I suppose he could be classed as a man'.

'Just about', smiled Geoff. 'But what are you doing about booze?'

'Admission — one bottle'.

'Should be good', said Geoff.

'With all the hard work of shifting armchairs about and stuff like that, it had better be!'

CHAPTER 17

PARTY PIECE

The drama group were rehearsing for the last time before the show. David and Geoff were sitting on a table discussing the script. Geoff looked over to Mr Dane. 'Will there be any parents coming?' he asked.

'For the show you mean?' enquired Mr Dane. 'No, I don't think so, it's just the kids and the teachers'.

'Oh, I see', commented Geoff.

'But there's one thing that bothers me', said Mr Dane, 'I just hope everyone remembers their lines.'

'So do I' agreed David. The lines were not the only thing that bothered him. He knew that Geoff and himself would have no trouble, after all, they did write most of them. But he was worried about everything, the lights, the curtains, the props, but his worry was probably brought on by the butterflies that were beginning to build up in his stomach.

'Don't worry', said Geoff, 'everything will go just great'.
David nodded, he hoped it would.

That Friday night just after school, David invited Ian to his party. Ian did not seem very keen. 'If I come, I'll come. Otherwise I'll see you on Monday, all right?' he said. He turned and walked off down the road.

'He doesn't seem very keen does he?' said David.

'No he doesn't', agreed Geoff with a smile. 'Perhaps he doesn't fancy spending the evening looking at your ugly face'.

David smiled. 'Come on', he said, 'come to my house and I'll show you my party list'.

'All right', said Geoff.

The two boys walked across the road and towards David's house. David took his key out and opened the door. Geoff followed him in to the bottom room. In the centre of the room was a small pile of decorations. David frowned, 'they've fallen down', he said, 'hang on a minute'. He disappeared out of the room. In a few seconds he came back with some steps and a packet of drawing pins. He put the steps up, took his coat off and threw it onto one of the chairs. He then picked up a handful of decorations and climbed the steps and proceeded to pin them onto the ceiling.

Geoff looked round the room. David had put up a few more things since the day before. Hanging from the ceiling in one corner was a small, square piece of cardboard covered with cooking foil, on it were painted the words 'Merry Christmas'. Above the record player and nailed across one of the two alcoves was a plank. On the outside it was also covered with cooking foil, but after inspection Geoff saw that on the inside were two coloured bulbs, one red and one blue.

'I see you fixed some lights up then', said Geoff.

'Yes', said David pinning up the last paper chain, 'I did it last night. Not bad, eh?' The lights were devised so that when switched on they would shine down on to the back of the record player.

'No, not bad', agreed Geoff. 'How many people are coming?'

David came down off the steps and took a list off the mantle-piece. He handed it to Geoff who looked down the list of perhaps forty people. 'It'll be good if everyone turns up. Do you think they will?'

'I hope so', said David.

Geoff folded the paper up and put it back down on the mantle-piece.

'What's all the foil for?' he asked.

'Well', said David, 'I thought that if I put up some foil it would help reflect the light around the room. But it doesn't. He demonstrated by switching on the coloured lights and turning off the main ones. Instantly the room was engulfed in a deep red and dark blue light. Geoff stood in the middle of the room and looked round. He was impressed.

'You know', he said, 'it looks really great'.

David smiled, 'Yeah, it does', he said proudly.

Ian had decided to go to the party after all and he had gone round to Roverhill House to get Geoff; they went along to David Cook's house. It was snowing lightly and it was very cold. The two boys walked quickly along. They stopped off at the 'off-licence' and bought two bottles of cider. It was 7.30 when Geoff knocked on the door of 78 Little Turner Street. The door was opened by Kim (the girl from Judo).

'Excuse me', said Geoff, 'but is this the annual antiception meeting on behalf of the 'Save the Fungi Campaign'.

The girl laughed and shook her head.

'It isn't!' exclaimed Geoff. 'Holy Winston Churchill', he turned to the grinning Ian. 'I'm terribly sorry old boy but it appears that we have come to the wrong establishment'.

David came out into the passage. 'Hallo Shorty', he said, 'come in'. Geoff and Ian walked into the passage.

'All the coats upstairs on my bed', he said. Geoff and Ian walked through the small group of people standing in the passage and went upstairs and put their coats on the bed and then came down again. Geoff knew most of the people in the group. There was Michael, his brother Stephen and David's cousins (they were twins) Robert and Kevin. There were also three other boys but Geoff did not know them. To Ian, they were all strangers as he had never met any of them before.

Geoff said a few words to Michael and then the two boys walked into the noisy room. The thick red curtains were drawn and the room was in complete darkness save for the red and blue lights. There were perhaps twenty people in the room. A group over by the drinks table, a few girls sitting on the seats. A few people including David were dancing in the middle of the room. Michael and the people outside had come in and were sitting on the long cushions next to the record player. George was over by the corner talking to two girls. He left them and walked over to the table to get himself a drink. George jumped when Geoff slapped him on the back. 'Hello George', he said. 'Who are those two girls you were chatting up'.

George coolly filled his glass with cider, 'I'm not chatting them up, I brought them here', he said, lifting the glass up to his lips.

'Who are they then?' asked Geoff, straining in the dim light to look at the girls.

'They live in the flats opposite me. Their names are Sandra — the one with the blue smock on — and the blonde one's Christine'.

'I see you decided to let someone else look at them then?' said Geoff sarcastically.

'Not that you'll get a look in', replied George with equal spite.

There was a knock at the door. 'Don't worry, I'll get it', shouted someone above the noise of the stereo. David turned down the record player to welcome the new guests. There were two of them — Diana and Evelyn. They were old friends of David's. Diana was a small, shy girl but very goodlooking. She sat down quietly in the corner. Evelyn was plain and on the plump side. Once she had settled in at a party (David's was no exception) she would become very noisy. She was even worse when she had been drinking. The girls were quickly introduced and Evelyn decided to have a game of darts (in a crowded room). After running riot with the darts, she soon grew tired of her game (a rather dangerous one as she started throwing them at the nearest posterior) and marched over to the drinks table.

'Would you like a drink, my delicate bundle of fun', asked David sarcastically.

'Knickers!' came the loud answer.

'Oh', said Geoff, 'such a sweet tongue the child has'. He quickly vanished out of the room.

Evelyn walked over to the record player and rather heavy-handedly began to look through the records. 'Have you got any

115

Gary Glitter?' she asked, sifting through the records that were beginning to bend under the strain.

'Look', said David, watching her wreck his record collection, 'why don't you dance with someone and I'll find you a Gary Glitter record'.

She turned to David who thought for one frightening moment that she was going to hit him. 'There's no-one to dance with', she argued.

'There's enough boys', said David. He was beginning to wonder why he had ever let her come in the first place.

'But I don't want to dance with boys', she said.

David was losing his temper. 'Oh, I'm so sorry madam', he said loudly, 'but the gorillas haven't turned up yet'.

She thought for some unknown reason that the remark was funny. She giggled and gave David a playful tap on the arm which sent him crashing into the record player.

George, who had been standing around Sandra and Christine much like a mother hen does when protecting her chicks, was angered when Geoff came over and asked Christine for a dance. She looked at George and then seemed to make up her mind and nodded. Geoff led her to the middle of the room. George grunted and marched out of the room and slammed the door. David followed him. A few seconds later he came back in and walked over to Geoff.

'What's up with George?' asked Geoff, looking over Christine's shoulder.

'He said he's going home'.

'Why?'

'He wouldn't say, but knowing him, it's because Christine's dancing with you. So he's got the hump'.

Because George promised the two girls' mothers that he, and no-one else would take them home, Sandra and Christine had to go with him. Unfortunately for Geoff, who was beginning to enjoy himself. George came into the room carrying the girls' coats. He said nothing as he waited for Sandra and Christine to put them on. He ignored the offensive comments made by Geoff and David. He muttered his goodbyes and walked swiftly out of the room and waited with the street door open for the girls to finish their goodbyes. A few minutes later the front door slammed. David sat down on the cushion and thought. He didn't like what George had done. It had been hard work organising the room and he did not like people taking him for granted like George. He soon forgot about the whole thing.

After about half an hour of making everyone's life a misery, Evelyn started to quieten down and she mixed in with the party.

David put on a slow record. Geoff asked Diana for a dance. She nodded and they joined the other five or so couples dancing in the middle of the room.

Geoff held Diana close to him and they swayed gently to the soft music that drifted out of the record player. He slowly turned round to see David dancing with Kim. He had put a few records on the spindle so he did not have to keep going over to change them. Geoff kissed Diana on the cheek and then on the lips. She looked at him and smiled. A few dances later she whispered, 'We'd better go out into the passage. It's dark there'. Geoff kissed her again and then the two disappeared out of the room.

It was 12.30 when (after a few people had to be taken home because of drinking too much) everyone decided to go home, or in some cases, stagger. The main light had been turned on and the coloured ones off. The record player was still on.

Michael, Ian, David and Geoff were tidying up and putting the furniture back. Geoff noticed Ian was grinning like a cheshire cat.

'What are you grinning for?' he asked.

Ian picked up a glass from the floor and put it on the table. 'It's just that when you were out in the passage fighting off Christine, and David was in the bedroom with Kim, I was in the bathroom with Evelyn'.

David laughed with surprise. 'In the bathroom!' he exclaimed. 'With that lump?'

'So what's wrong with that?' said Ian defensively. 'She's alright'.

'Yeah, she's alright', smiled Geoff, 'if yer like elephants'.

The insults were stopped when Ian threw a paper cup at Geoff.

The boys cleared up and Ian, Geoff and Michael put on their coats.

'It wasn't a bad party, was it?' said Michael.

'Not bad at all', agreed Geoff.

The boys said goodbye and David watched as they walked up the street and turned the corner.

CHAPTER 18

SPECTACULAR

It was Christmas. The season of goodwill to all men. It was the time of year when people who usually went around attacking other people, or stealing things, start being good, kind, generous and loving. Well, for one day at least.

Sheila was one of these people. A few weeks earlier she had thrown a fire extinguisher through a window after losing her temper. Geoff and David had got used to her tantrums. At first it was a bit frightening, but now it did not worry them so much, as most of the children in Selton had violent tempers. Even Geoff and David. In Selton, if someone threatened to throw a chair at somebody else, the threat was not ignored. Geoff himself had thrown a paintbox through the Art Room window when someone started throwing paint at him. But then it was a school for children with problems, and nearly always part of the problem was a violent temper.

Throughout the year, almost half the children would play truant. As Christmas began to appear, so did the children. At Christmas the school began to take on a much friendlier atmosphere, building up as the last .day of term and the show came much closer.

A few days before the show, Mrs Cox (the teacher of the tutorial class) had phoned Mr Reed to tell him that the class was having a party that afternoon and asked if he would let David and Geoff have the afternoon off so they could go. Mr Reed said 'yes' and sent a message down to the two boys. They were helping Mr Walker, the woodwork teacher in the coal-cellar. The reason for this was that Mr Walker had decided to put some huge concrete pots with flowers in them in the top playground to make it 'look nicer'.

David, Geoff, Ian and Kevin Scott, a huge boy of about Geoff's age, were helping him. Because the pots were so heavy, Mr Walker decided to use the manually operated lift that was once used to take coal up to the Headmaster's office. They were having a lot of trouble; firstly because the pots were bigger than the lift, (it was no more than a platform with an iron-type fence that went up to waist level to stop the coal from falling out), they had to be laid on their sides, and secondly, because the pots were bowl-shaped, some brave volunteer had to go in the lift to make sure they did not roll about. Geoff being the lightest was made to go up with the pots. Reluctantly Geoff squeezed into the lift and held on to the first pot.

Mr Walker, Ian, David and Kevin pulled on the rope and the nervous Geoff and pot started slowly rising up the fifty-foot lift shaft. The lift had just gone past the headmaster's office when suddenly it started to descend, gaining speed all the time. Fortunately for Geoff, the lift had a brake which enabled him to stop it. The lift, with Geoff and the pot had to be pulled up from the top, and Geoff waited for a frightening five minutes wondering if he would plunge thirty-five feet to the cellar, whilst Mr Walker and the three boys raced up the stairs to haul him from the top playground. After this, the pots were sent up on their own. Mr Walker had found the fault in the lift and they were just sending the last lot up when the message from Mr Reed came to Geoff and David in the shape of Teresa Doves. The two boys enjoyed the party at the tutorial class. They had a chance to see Simon and John again. And they told Mrs Cox all about Selton, after which they had gone back to 78 Little Turner Street to put the final touches to the script of the Drama Group's show — their 'spectacular'.

It had finally come, the last day of term and the show. It was one-thirty and David, Geoff, Ian and the rest of the class were going through the messy task of having make-up put on them.

Mr Dane was helping Mrs Buckley, and they were doing the job well. Michael Smith, one of the younger boys of Selton looked tough before putting on the make-up, but after having lipstick and powder put on him, he looked more like Marilyn Munroe. Mr Dane approached Geoff armed with powder and lipstick and started to dab his face with it; Geoff pushed his hand away and ran over to the door, 'Not me, Dane', he said. 'I'm not having any powder on me, it's poofy'.

This view was also shared by David and Ian. They thought they would look effeminate with make-up on.

'We'll be going on stage with handbags and flowers next', said David, as a powder puff came whizzing in his direction. He ducked, 'You missed', he laughed.

'Come on', said Mrs Buckley, 'stop being a big baby and get ready'.

Reluctantly the boys agreed to have make-up put on them. It was two o'clock when they went down to make the final preparations to the stage and props.

Kevin Scott, who was given the job of controlling the curtains, sat at the side of the stage holding the ropes. This was also where the cast sat waiting to go on.

Mrs Buckley and Mr Dane took up seats at the side of the

stage. Mrs Buckley was the prompter. There were still a few more children in the cast to come. Geoff peeped through a gap in the curtain at the forty or so children and teachers. 'We've got a full house', he said, feeling a sudden attack of butterflies. He turned back to David who was sitting on a table at the back of the stage (the table was the main prop) reading a Playboy magazine. 'What's that?' asked Geoff. David held up the magazine, 'It helps calm the nerves', he smiled.

Geoff sat down next to him and looked at the magazine. And it was precisely at that moment that Kevin thought he would play a joke and he opened the curtains. The audience sat up and watched David and Geoff drooling over one of the pictures. Because they were looking down, they did not see that the curtains were open, they just kept on discussing the physical dimensions of one of the pin-ups. This went on for a full twenty seconds, with all the cast trying to get the boys' attention. Finally someone closed the curtains. When the boys found out what had happened they nearly fainted and had to sit down for a few minutes.

At last the rest of the cast came (they were in the toilet) and everything was ready. The 'spectacular' was about to begin.

The curtains opened again. This time at the right moment. The younger children were first on. Three boys and two girls stood round in a wide circle. Two boys came on, the bigger one holding the smaller one on his back. He was the horse. Mrs Buckley made a fake galloping noise by hitting two boxes together. The 'horse' and rider came to the first boy (like the rest, he was dressed as a housewife). They stopped, 'Is your husband home?' shouted the rider.

'Yes', came the answer.

'Well tell him to be ready to fight, the enemy's coming'.

This went on with four housewives until the last one.

'Is your husband home?' came the shout.

'No'.

'Woa!' The horse stopped.

The audience laughed and the curtains closed again. They opened to show Geoff sitting at the table wearing a blue hat, much like an air hostess and a blue jacket, a silk scarf with the letters 'I.R' round his neck and shoulders. He was 'Zeff Tracy' the chief of 'Blunderbirds'.

'John!' shouted Geoff.

There was a voice from off the stage, 'What?'

'Get your arse in here' came the rude command.

Ian came onto the stage dressed the same as Geoff. He was walking (or supposed to) like a puppet. 'Yes father?' asked Ian in a mock American accent.

'There's an important assignment', said Geoff, 'it's out in the Sahara desert. Some silly beggar's gone and blown himself up and he's trapped in a cave with an unexploded bomb'.

'I'm on my way father', said Ian.

Geoff jumped up. 'Not so bloody fast! We don't want them to think we actually like risking our necks just to save some miserable bum that's gone and got himself into a mess'.

'No father', Ian turned to walk away but was called back.

'And the next time you take Sin-Sin to the pictures in Blunderbird I, make sure you let me know first'.

'Why father?' asked Ian. 'What was the matter, I had my driving licence with me'.

'What was the matter?' exclaimed Geoff, 'What was the matter? I'll tell you what was the matter my lad. When that bloody great chunk of machinery's gonna take off, that swimming pool it's underneath slides away'.

'Yes I know father'.

'Well you don't bother to see if there's anybody in the pool at the time do you? I nearly got crushed to death when you were taking off'.

'Well I'm sorry father', said Ian trying to hold back the laughter.

'Don't give me that', shouted Geoff. 'You loved every minute of it. Now where's that gay son of mine, Virgin?'

This was David's cue to enter. Not as Virgin, but as the master mind behind the whole organisation— 'Drains'.

David was perfect for this role as he had the right intellectual-looking face. And when he borrowed a pair of thick horn-rimmed spectacles, he definitely looked the master-mind.

'Er, g-gee m-m-mister Tracey, I-I think we're g-gonna n-need the automatic Gonosher Gonosher f-for this o-one', he said, also in an American accent.

Geoff looked surprised. 'What the bloody hell's that?' he asked.

'W-well', came the stuttered answer, 'I'll try t-to e-explain it as simply as I-I can Mister Tracy'.

'Please do'.

'You s-see', said David really looking the part. The audience were laughing. 'It's an a-automatic n-n-n . . .'

'Knickers?'

'Nuclear device that e-enables the w-wave length to c-c-c . . .'

'Contraception?'

'C-c-c . . .'

'Constipation?'

'C-cross examine the e-electronic controlled s-scanning visor, thus increasing the p-power of the s-solar energy cells. That s-starts a ch-chain reaction of the subterranean m-molecular o-osophegus in the st-structure of the b-brick and r-rock itself'.

The audience laughed at the complete nonsense speech that David had just delivered. There was a pause.

'That's the one thing I like about you, Drains', said Geoff admiringly, 'Your clear precise way of talking, the way you come to the point'. He turned to Ian. 'Now don't you wish you could talk like that instead of saying 'Yes father' and 'no father' all the time?'

'Yes father'.

Teresa Doves who had been waiting off-stage for her cue jumped on and strolled over to Geoff.

'Ah, Sin-Sin my lovely little nymphet. Where have you been?'

'Oh, I've been walking through the woods with Alan'.

'Oh terrific', said Geoff sarcastically, 'We've got an important mission and you've been tiring him out. And where's Virgin? You haven't seen him have you?

'He was with the butler the last time I saw him', answered Teresa.

'Blimey!' said Geoff, 'What an organisation'.

The curtain closed for a few seconds then opened again to show Geoff, David and Ian trying their hardest to act out a scene from a recent comedy programme. This was Ian's idea, so naturally it all went wrong. No-one laughed.

The curtain closed yet again. This time when they opened the audience saw Geoff standing behind the table holding some sheets of paper. He was wearing a black beret, dark glasses, a green waistcoat and his trouser legs were tucked in the top of his socks. It was time for his solo performance. It started after Mr Hamilton shouted to one of the boys in the audience 'put that fag out'.

Geoff cleared his throat and read out a piece of poetry he himself had written. It went like this:

There's a man who fights for righteousness,
If there's evil to be chased,
You'll always see this man about
Because that's when he shows his face.

He isn't Captain Marvel,
And he isn't Billy Whizz.
And he's definitely not the 'fantastic four'
For those who think he is.

He's known quite simply as 'Archibald',
A lavatory attendant,
But if evil he spies,
He would don guise of 'Super Strop' defendant.

One day as Arch clocked into work
He went into his toilet,
The shining pan was spick and span
And he did not like to spoil it.

Then from his secret cistern came a cry of evil caper,
It frightened Archibald so much, he dropped his toilet paper.
'This is a job for Super-Strop!' Archy proudly cried,
So he put on his bonnet with GLC on it, armed
With ball cock by his side.

He pulled his secret chain, and waited a few seconds or more
Then as quick as a wink, a porcelain sink appeared from
Under the floor.

Archy climbed upon it, feeling proud and brave.
He pulled his chain, and yet again it moved
Towards his cave.

The Super, Secret, Strop bike stood inside its cell
It had a peddle missing and it creaked a bit, but it
Served its master well.

Archy jumped upon his bike and peddled but stood
Still.
Until he found the reason why: he only had one wheel.

'I'll kill that bleeding superman, he always has to
Spoil it!
I think I'll give him sandpaper, when he comes to
Use my toilet'.

Archy had to hurry,
He had not time to swear or curse, if he was to be
In time for the scene of the crime, he had to catch a bus.

He waited at the bus-stop, until the bus came over the hill,
'You can't get on here', laughed the conductor,
'You want the batmobile'.

So insulted was poor Archy to what the man had said.
He reached in for his ball cock and hit him on the head.

Rejected and heartbroken, his hopes crushed to the ground
Super Strop slunk away, with his ball cock dangling down.

The audience clapped and cheered Geoff for his poem until the next item on the show started. David did not know it, but this was to turn out to be *his* solo performance. The item was a song-cum-dramatic speech. Geoff went to the front of the stage. David stood just behind him playing an imaginary violin consisting of a ruler on his left shoulder. The audience was quiet. Geoff began to sing, 'When this bloody war is over'. The idea was that Geoff would end up saying the words like a dramatic speech on the battlefields in the Great War. He sang two verses then began his speech. He went down on his knees as if he was crying out to God. The audience was a little surprised by this action. 'Oh God! Oh God!' cried Geoff, 'when this bloody war is over, I shall go home to my mother and our beautiful home in the country . . .'

He was doing very well. He then jumped off the stage and wandered around the audience. Meanwhile David was still playing the violin as if nothing had happened. Geoff went over to Mr Reed and got a great reaction from the school when he started to 'cry' on the headmaster's shoulder. He did this to about five other teachers. Then still giving his tear-jerking plea from the heart, he staggered out of the far entrance of the hall. The idea was for Geoff to run down the stairs, along the playground, up the other staircase and come staggering into the hall from the entrance near the stage, still performing his hilarious speech. But because this was so well rehearsed and Geoff was doing it, it all went wrong. He had gone out of the hall, down the stairs and along the playground to the other staircase, but someone had locked the door. So poor Geoff had to go back along to the first staircase, run up to the top playground, across then down the stairs to the hall. It had all gone well when Geoff had gone out of the hall, but after a while David began to feel and look rather silly standing there humming and playing a ruler and a right shoulder. He began to sweat. What had happened? Had Geoff fallen down the stairs and injured himself so much that he could not move? The audience by now had become rather impatient. Somebody whistled and shouted and everyone started to talk. David then began to think that he had become a victim of a rather unfunny joke. Geoff had gone home! What went wrong? He started to shuffle uncomfortably. Mrs Buckley whispered from off stage, 'Keep going Dave, you're doing fine'. David Cook did not think so.

In fact, he felt as if he were going to die. Just then, like a knight in shining armour, Geoffrey Moller Esquire came staggering in to rescue his friend. He was still delivering his plea from the heart. David and the rest of the drama group gave a sigh of relief.

'Some twit locked the bloody door', shouted Geoff.

Everyone realised what had happened and, fortunately for the drama group, they started to laugh. He jumped up on to the stage and the curtain closed.

'What's next?' asked Geoff.

'Ernie', someone answered.

For the next item all the group were going to perform 'Ernie, the fastest milkman in the west'.

The curtains opened and the audience saw David sitting on a chair wearing a flat hat too big for his head. He was the lead. Four others knelt around him — they were the chorus. While David and the chorus were performing the song, Ian, Geoff and Teresea Doves acted out the words with hilarious consequences; When Ernie (Geoff) and Ted (Ian), Ernie's arch enemy, had a showdown to see who would marry Sue (Teresa), the yogurts and buns never hit their target. Ernie was killed by a rock cake and Ted eventually married Sue. That was when it all went wrong. Ernie's ghost appeared on Ted and Sue's wedding night, as rehearsed, but the deceased Ernie tripping over a yogurt and falling flat on his face, was not. He picked himself up, walked over to David and tapped him on the shoulder.

'Could you do that last bit again?' he asked.

Everyone burst out laughing and David obliged. They still got their applause. It all went well, even though there was no music. The spectacular came to a hilarious end.

David sat at the table pretending to play the piano (When it came to imaginary instruments, David was a genius). Geoff came to the front of the stage and started to thank everyone. As he called out the names of the people in the drama group they came on the stage and bowed. When Geoff had called out the last name, he should have finished. But no, then he read out every name in the school. He then read out the names of the West Ham football team and thanked the Queen, God and the Pope for not coming to the play. And last of all he thanked David Cook. Then all the cast of spectacular sang 'Old Lang Syne'.

Mr Reed stood up and walked up to the stage and made a small speech about how much he enjoyed the show, even when it went wrong. He told everyone when the new term was to start and he said he hoped David would make a few more appearances.

And last of all, he hoped everyone had a very nice enjoyable Christmas. Everybody cheered and Mr Reed walked off the stage and out of the school with the rest of the school, leaving the drama class to the clearing up.

David went over to one of the windows and looked out of it. He was pleased. The show hadn't been perfect, but everyone had enjoyed themselves. Geoff came over to him. He said.

'The play was funny wasn't it!'

David nodded and turned around.

'You know', said Geoff, 'we've done some funny things these past few years, haven't we?'

'Yes' replied David looking round the hall. 'We should write a book about it some day'.

OTHER PUBLICATIONS

From the Basement Writers

The Boxer Speaks: Odes and Poems -- A collection of poems by an elderly ex-boxer from Stepney, poems about days in the ring, about life in the East End and about the economic poverty of old people. 15p plus 5p postage.

Follow Me — Collection of poems by a Stepney school-student, partly religious, exploratory in theme. 15p plus 5p postage.

Never Had It So Good — Tough, satirical poems about life in the East End by another school-student member of the Basement Writers. 15p plus 5p postage.

From Centerprise

Vivian Usherwood: Poems -- Collection of poems by a thirteen year old boy from the West Indies about his friends, his home, and school. 10p plus 5p postage.

Christine Gillies: Poems — Collection by a local young woman, mainly about relationships with other people. 10p plus 5p postage.

Home For Tea — Forty poems by a local mother, mostly about her three young children. Illustrated with very fine line drawings. 15p plus 5p postage.

Stepney Words 1 & 2 — Collected edition combining the two original anthologies of East End children's poetry. Illustrated with photographs by Ron McCormick and line drawings by Jimmy May. 35p plus 8p postage.

A Hoxton Childhood — An autobiographical account of a working class childhood in the East End of London. 50p plus 10p postage.

Years of Change — The autobiography of a Hackney shoe-maker covering the years 1900-1965. A unique insight into nearly one hundred years of working class life. 35p plus 10p postage.

A Licence to Live: Scenes from a post-war working life in Hackney — The autobiography of a local taxi-driver, from his earliest childhood and experience of evacuation, through his thirty-seven jobs to his present work. An important piece of contemporary working class writing. 35p plus 10p postage.

All of these books and a complete list of other publications available from the Centerprise Publishing Project, 136 Kingsland High Street, London E8.